MATHS
GAMES
2
KEY STAGE TWO

Shape, Space & Measures

Joe Santaniello

MATHS
KEY STAGE TWO 2
GAMES

Published by Scholastic Ltd.,
Villiers House, Clarendon Avenue,
Leamington Spa, Warwickshire CV32 5PR
© 1995 Scholastic Ltd.

AUTHOR Joe Santaniello
EDITOR Jo Saxelby-Jennings
ASSISTANT EDITOR Joanne Boden
SERIES DESIGNER Joy White
DESIGNER Toby Long
ILLUSTRATIONS Mike Miller
(Black Sheep Design)
COVER ARTWORK Joy White

Designed using Aldus Pagemaker
Printed in Great Britain by Bell & Bain Ltd, Glasgow

British Library Cataloguing-in-Publication Data
A catalogue record for this book is available from the British Library.

ISBN 0-590-53361-4

Contents

Contents...

MATHS
GAMES
2
KEY STAGE
TWO

Introduction

THE CONTRIBUTION OF GAMES TO TEACHING AND LEARNING

We live in a games-saturated culture. Outdoor sports and computer games are obvious examples at opposite ends of a spectrum that encompasses our everyday life. Games appeal to all sections of society, and are, therefore, levellers of difference. But games are often ephemeral. We play them, we forget them. Perhaps it is this transience which makes some teachers and parents sceptical of the value games have in learning. Games in school are often relegated to a peripheral role, as time-fillers or rewards for having completed 'important' work. The books in this series are an attempt to counterbalance this viewpoint by showing how games with clear learning objectives can be brought into the mainstream of primary teaching, to help develop key concepts and skills alongside any scheme of work.

In the context of mathematics teaching, games serve a number of educational purposes, providing an alternative forum for:
- using and applying mathematical skills and understanding;
- discussing mathematical concepts and developing mathematical language;
- developing the ability to follow instructions;
- developing co-operative learning, social and problem-solving skills;
- increasing motivation and subject interest;
- encouraging independence;
- bridging the gap between practical activities and more abstract methods of recording;
- assessing acquisition of skills and knowledge.

The games in this series of books also offer the following benefits. They:
- have clear educational objectives linked to the National Curriculum programmes of study and the Scottish 5–14 Guidelines;
- save time and money by providing photocopiable resources;
- can be adapted to suit individual needs and purposes;
- offer suggestions for differentiation;
- include game record sheets to promote data handling and record-keeping, and to provide evidence;
- have lively real-life and imaginary contexts to capture and hold the children's interest.

GAMES AND THE MATHEMATICS CURRICULUM

All of these games have been devised to support mathematics requirements in the National Curriculum and the Scottish 5–14 Guidelines. A vital element of many traditional games is the reinforcement of counting and number recognition skills. The games in this series build on these acknowledged benefits, extending them into less well-explored areas of the mathematics curriculum within an atmosphere of pleasurable learning. The children's imagination is captured by interlacing the mathematical content with role-playing in both 'real' and fantasy worlds. The games provide a collaborative forum for discussion and, therefore, a focus for asking questions and developing mathematical language. The decision-making, prediction and reasoning skills outlined in Using and Applying Mathematics (Attainment Target 1) are developed in all the games, and the inclusion of game record sheets ensures that data handling is integrated throughout.

THE GAMES

This book contains both non-board based games (in the section called Activity Games) as well as games that use boards and other manipulative resources (in the sections called Photocopiable Games and Special Section).

ACTIVITY GAMES

This section provides a selection of ideas for games that only require resources commonly found in classrooms. Most of the games can be played by the whole class. Some are physical activity games and are best played in a large open space such as a hall, playground or field.

PHOTOCOPIABLE GAMES

The games in this section are based on photocopiable resources that are provided. These resources include game boards (some of which have a three-dimensional element), cards, game rules, game record sheets, and playing components such as spinners and playing pieces. These games follow traditional game formats and are designed to be played in small groups. The 'make-your-own' feature of the photocopiable sheets means that games can be adapted easily and without great expense.

When making the playing pieces, cut along solid lines and fold along dotted lines.

The following symbols are used on some of the photocopiable pages:

 A calculator may be useful.

 For construction, the sheet needs to be photocopied the number of times shown.

SPECIAL SECTION

This section contains photocopiable resources to be used with games from the Photocopiable Games section. They also have wider applications for other mathematical and cross-curricular activities.

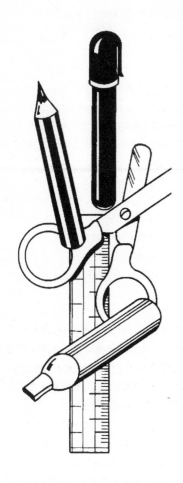

THE TEACHERS' NOTES

The teachers' notes follow a standard format for each game:

TEACHING CONTENT

The mathematical learning objectives are signposted and linked to the National Curriculum programmes of study for Key Stage Two and the Scottish 5–14 Guidelines. For example: **(SSM 4a; ME: D)** indicates National Curriculum Attainment Target **S**hape, **s**pace and **m**easures: Key Stage Two programme of study paragraph **4a**; Scottish 5–14 Guidelines for Number, money and measurement, strand **M**easure and **e**stimate, Level **D**.

WHAT YOU NEED

Resources that you will need are listed under the following headings: 'Photocopiable sheets', 'For construction' and 'For playing'.

PREPARATION

Notes are given on assembling the game and, where appropriate, suggestions made for introducing the game.

HOW TO PLAY

The aims and rules of the game are briefly summarised and any additional information for the teacher to consider is pointed out.

TEACHER'S ROLE

In some of the games the teacher is an active participant, in others a facilitator or an observer. This section helps the teacher to define her role and offers ideas for developing the game's mathematical ideas and skills. See also Page 9.

GAME VARIATIONS

Where a game can be varied within the mathematical objectives set out under the 'Teaching content', ideas are given.

EXTENSION

Where a game might be extended to develop the mathematical objectives, ideas are given.

ASSESSMENT

There are three main ways that the teacher can assess the value of a game and the children's learning:

• Direct observation of the game in progress
Observation of a game allows the teacher to note how each child copes with the skills required in the game. A clipboard is handy for on-the-spot jotting down of notes. Be aware, however, that an adult presence can distort the game.

• Discussion after the game
After the game, the supervising adult can discuss what happened with the group, extending the players' horizons beyond 'who won' mentality.

Where appropriate, pointers and suggested questions for doing this are given in the teachers' notes.

• Using game record sheets

Many games are accompanied by a game record sheet upon which the result and how it was achieved can be recorded by the players themselves, giving concrete evidence of how well they have assimilated the concept(s) behind the game. The game record sheets employ writing, drawing and data-handling skills to give the busy teacher an outline of the completed game; in many cases, these sheets can be adapted to provide differentiation for the games.

CLASSROOM MANAGEMENT

As indicated above, not all the games are board games. There are card games, pencil and paper games, calculator games and mental games. This variety enables the teacher to select the appropriate game for the particular classroom situation, or even for sending home to be played with parents. Group games can be played at a table or designated corner. Some games are suitable for individual play – a copy of a single track, for instance, can be used both as a playing surface and as a record of the game – with the child competing against herself.

THE TEACHERS' ROLE

The teachers' main task will be in the selection of the game and the setting up of play for the designated educational purpose. She will need to decide what curricular function the game can serve. It can introduce a subject; it can reinforce skills or knowledge already touched on; or it can be a means of assessment; suggestions for carrying this out are given, where appropriate, within the teachers' notes for each game.

Unless the children have played the game before, or are competent readers and can play well together on their own, the teacher (or another adult) will need to introduce and supervise the games. Ideas for introducing the games are given, where appropriate, in the teachers' notes to provide a context or stimulus for playing the game. Alternatively, the teacher can make up her own.

There is no sense in letting the children play a game and then forget it. It needs to be followed up. In the teachers' notes for each game, there are suggestions about the part the supervising adult can play in enlarging the players' horizons beyond the actual playing of the game.

Obviously, the light of experience will indicate possible variations to the games, and the photocopiable pages enable the teacher to alter details and change rules to match individual needs and purposes.

MAKING AND STORING THE GAMES

Photocopiable games are flexible and inexpensive. Even elaborate board games can be made for pence, whereas comparable commercial games could cost pounds. Also, little more than the usual art materials found in most schools is needed for their construction. So instead of having just a few games to enhance motivation and learning, the teacher can afford to be quite lavish with them.

If possible, photocopy the game boards and playing pieces directly on to card.

The appearance and motivational benefit of the games can be greatly improved by colouring them in. Felt-tipped pens are best as they don't warp the paper as much as paint. Laminating the game boards and pieces also improves appearance and increases durability.

Mathematics games

• Making the most of parents and educational assistants
There is no reason why the teacher needs to do all the assembling. Games construction is a pleasurable activity involving colouring-in, cutting, pasting and, optionally laminating. None of these tasks requires a teaching certificate! Parents, and even older pupils in the school, are quite capable of doing these things. Organise a games-making event involving both parents, helpers and pupils!

Similarly, a parent can be the games supervisor, instructing the group in the rules of the game, keeping an eye on its progress and conducting the discussion afterwards.

• Storing the games
Keep the various components of each game (board, pieces, game record sheets, 'How to play' sheets, and so on) in a polythene bag, fastened with a wire tie. These can be attached to a 'mathematics games' board with a small bulldog clip (as shown in the illustration). Alternatively, the games can be stored in boxes – either kept individually or grouped according to difficulty in a large box and separated using coloured dividers.

ADAPTING THE GAMES

Photocopiable games are easily adapted. They can be changed to suit different purposes and abilities. You need not be stuck with a resource that only meets a small percentage of your requirements. Just delete the bit you don't want by covering with liquid paper or a sticky label, then draw and/or print your modification on top. If you are altering very fine detail, enlarge the sheet before making the alterations. Do your alterations on the enlargement, making sure to draw the lines the same density and thickness as the enlargement. Then reduce back to original size. Similarly, if a game is too big or too small, it can be altered to size using the enlarging or reducing facility on most large photocopiers. If yours can't do this, ones that can will be found in most public libraries.

Simple alterations such as writing children's names on playing pieces or using the school logo on the headings may seem small things in themselves, but they make the games more personal and special.

Copies of each adaptation can be kept in polypockets in an A4 ring binder devoted to the purpose. A slip of paper or card can be put in the pocket detailing when the adaptation was made, its curriculum focus, which class used it, notes on how effective it was and further ideas for adaptation.

CROSS-CURRICULAR CONNECTIONS

As many of the games involve role-playing and have suitable contexts to develop storylines, they fit easily into language topics. Some of the games will readily integrate with other subject areas – for example, 'Trees' and 'Temperature control' with science and 'Anywhere' with geography. Ideas for these, where appropriate, are offered in the 'Preparation' or 'Teacher's role' sections of the teachers' notes.

LINKS TO THE NATIONAL CURRICULUM

★ main game
☆ extension

Games	Programmes of Study														
	1a	1b	1c	1e	2a	2b	2c	3a	3b	3c	4a	4b	4c	N1A	N4A
Croc chops				★						★					
Learner driver		★						★							
On the ball				★							★	★			
At full stretch	★										★		★		
Reflections							★								
Battleshapes						★			★						
Polly names					★	★									
Copy cats					★	★									
Shapes scavenger hunt	★					★									
Traffic jam											★				
Planting									★						
In the balance				★								★			
Measures mat				★							★	★			
Trees										★					
Temperature control												★			
Polly gone				★	★										
Polygon castle					★										
Snail's pace													★		
24 hours		★													★
Myself				★							★				
The lion and the rose			★								★☆		☆		
Guess what?				★							★	★			
Removals				★									★		
Anywhere									★						
Fruit											★	★			
UFO											★	★		★	
Roughly right		★									★				
Web				★								★			
Roto sym							★	★							
Wheels										★					
Expedition											★				
Boomerang								★	★						
Happy Birthday											★	★			
Euro tour											★	★			
The fairy ring										★					

LINKS TO SCOTTISH 5–14 GUIDELINES

★ main game
☆ extension

Games	A/B	A/D	ME A/B	ME C	ME D/E	PM B/C	PM D/E	T B	T C	T D	PFS D	RS B/C	RS D/E	S B	S D/E
Strands and attainment targets															
Croc chops	★														
Learner driver			★			★									
On the ball			★	★						★					
At full stretch				★	★						★		★		
Reflections														★	
Battleshapes						★						★	★		
Polly names													★		
Copy cats												★			
Shapes scavenger hunt												★			
Traffic jam				★											
Planting						★									
In the balance			★	★											
Measures mat				★					★						
Trees		★				★									
Temperature control				★	★										
Polly gone													★		
Polygon castle													★		
Snail's pace											★				
24 hours									★	★					
Myself					★										
The lion and the rose			☆	★☆	★										
Guess what?				★	★										
Removals					★										
Anywhere						★									
Fruit		★				★									
UFO		★													
Roughly right				★	★										
Web		★					★								
Roto sym															★
Wheels		★													
Expedition									★	★					
Boomerang						★	★								
Happy Birthday								★	★						
Euro tour							★								
The fairy ring						★	★								

Activity games

CROC CHOPS

TEACHING CONTENT

☆ Discovering right angles in the classroom (SSM: 1e; A: B)
☆ Using a simple quadrant for measuring a right angle (SSM: 3c; A: B)

PREPARATION

Make sufficient copies of the 'Croc Chops' sheet in the Special Section (photocopiable page 141) for every player to have her own. Preferably copy the sheet directly on to card, then cut out the 'chops' and assemble them with paper fasteners. Put sticky tape across the back of the fasteners to protect the children's fingers. A recording strip such as the one shown opposite would add to the game. If you wish, make a suitable A4 master sheet and copy one for every player.

Name:

Croc Chops ate:

in ☐ minutes.

HOW TO PLAY

This can be a class or large group game with each child participating individually. Give the players a set time in which to find as many examples of right angles around the classroom as they can, using their Croc Chops to check. If they are using a recording strip, encourage the children to list or draw the objects with right angles that they find. When the time limit is up, go over the lists with the children. They can score a point for each right angle correctly identified. Who has got the greediest Croc?

TEACHER'S ROLE

Before the game, discuss right angles and demonstrate their relationship to corners with Croc Chops. Explain that Croc Chops is a right-angle eater. Show the children how Croc Chops' eyes only open fully when he discovers one. Let them try their Croc Chops and see for themselves how, when the eye is fully aligned, the jaws are at right angles. Encourage the children to take home their Croc Chops quadrants to discover right angles there.

Extend the discussion after the game to include other mathematical measuring devices. Explain that 'maths machines' do not have to be covered with numbers, like a calculator or ruler. Some timers, for example, do not have numbers. Egg timers and rocker timers measure a specific period without recourse to numbers.

LEARNER DRIVER

TEACHING CONTENT

☆ Estimating and measuring distances in non-standard and metric units (SSM: 1b; ME: A/B)
☆ Working out routes (SSM: 3a; PM: B)

PREPARATION

A large scale version of this game can be played in the playground or hall with chalk lines marking out a roadway with turns to the right and left.

Use a large cardboard box as a car with two cuddly toys in it for a learner driver and a driving examiner. For a small scale version, the road can be drawn out on a large sheet of paper or card and a toy car pushed around. The turns in the road identify the beginnings and ends of stages along the route. Instead of turns, you could have a straight road with different coloured boxes as the reference points. However, the bendy road will distort the apparent distances and stretch the children's estimating skills. The two players or teams will also need paper and pencils in order to list all the stages of the route and write down their estimates of the length of each stage.

HOW TO PLAY

In this game two individuals or groups compete against each other to see which is the more accurate at estimating distances. Both teams or players have to estimate the distance from the start to the first turn or coloured box: the first stage. The players write down how far they think it is either in terms of lengths of the vehicle (the cardboard box or the toy car) or in metric units (metres for the large scale game or centimetres for the small version). Each group keeps its estimates hidden from the other. Now you have two alternatives:

•   either the children can measure the distance of the first stage by marking out vehicle lengths or measuring with a ruler or tape and check it against their estimates and then go on to estimate and measure stage two and so on;

•   or, they can estimate the lengths of all the stages without checking until the end, when all the stages are measured and comparisons made.

In either case, the difference between the players' estimates and the actual distances, whether too little or too much, is the error. Throughout, or at the end of the game, all the errors are recorded and added up. The player or team with the smallest total error wins. If the children estimate and measure one distance at a time, they will have their experience to draw upon, and their estimates should improve and their compounded errors should decrease as the game evolves.

TEACHER'S ROLE

Throughout, you should be on hand, but should not have to intervene. When the children have calculated their errors and decided who is the eventual winner, go over the measuring skills that have been employed. In effect, the children have completed a simple traverse – that is, they have gone from one place to another measuring the distance between them. The children could be asked to draw a sketch map of the route. They will have to work out the approximate angles between the turns by simple line of sight.

ON THE BALL

TEACHING CONTENT

☆ Measuring time and distance in real-life contexts (SSM: 1e; T: D/ME: C)
☆ Estimating distance in metres (SSM: 4a; ME: C)
☆ Using second timer and/or a measuring tape or trundle wheel (SSM: 4b; T: D/ME: B)

PREPARATION

A ball is the focus for these games which provide contexts for the measurement of length and time. Both are ideal to play outdoors. Divide the class into pairs. Give each pair a ball, and either a metre tape or trundle wheel and a piece of chalk, or a second timer or stop-watch. Half-way through the session, let the pairs swap over so that those who have been measuring distance can try measuring time and vice versa.

HOW TO PLAY

Tell the pairs with the tapes or trundle wheels that they are going to have a competition to find out who can throw the furthest in ten throws. They will be awarded one point per metre. The pair stand opposite each other, at a distance they decide they can handle, and chalk-mark where they are standing. Then one child in each pair has to throw the ball to the other, who has to catch it and then throw it back. The ball *must not* touch the ground. If they are successful, the pair can measure the distance between their chalk marks and count their points; for example, 20m gives 20 points. Then they can decide whether they want to be further apart or nearer for their next throw. It is up to them. Every successful throw which is caught counts, but an unsuccessful throw means no points. The skill for the players is to decide just how far they dare throw the ball. It is possible for two children who do not have a lot of catching skill to pick a comfortable distance and still win.

Meanwhile, the other pairs have a competition to see who can bounce and catch a ball for the longest. One player in each pair initially does the timing and then they swap, the other player must bounce the ball continually from a called 'start'. The timer is stopped when the player drops the ball or misses a catch. Each second counts for one point. When both players in each pair have had a go, the final positions are listed in order, most first.

There are numerous variations of these games. The pairs could be joined together as bigger teams and their points added to an aggregate score. The ball could be bounced against a wall and caught. The games could be combined and added to others in a 'Ball games Olympics'.

TEACHER'S ROLE

This game provides a context in which measurement is an integral part. Once the children have got the hang of the games, encourage them to make some kind of informal record showing how far each throw went and the number of failed throws. The children can then pick out the record throw for the class. Back in the classroom, make a block graph showing the throwing sequences in different colours, and from this the totals and the longest throws. This can be seen as an early experience of scale drawing. Similarly, the length of time the balls were bounced can be recorded and translated on to a block graph.

AT FULL STRETCH

TEACHING CONTENT

☆ Estimating and measuring lengths and distances (SSM: 4a; ME: C/D)
☆ Making perimeters of triangles (SSM: 4c; PPS: D)
☆ Using angles and lengths to make triangles (SSM: 1a; RS: D)

PREPARATION

Make 12 rings that will fit over the posts you have available. A plastic pop bottle cut horizontally into rings will suffice, but do remember to sandpaper the edges of the rings as the plastic may otherwise scratch the children's hands. Cut six lengths of string and tie a ring on to each end. The finished lengths should be: 2m, 4m, 6m, 8m, 10m and 12m. Tie one of the ribbons on to each. (The ribbons can be swapped about so that the children do not associate a particular colour with a particular length.) Put the strings in the box. Convert the play brick into a colour dice by sticking the coloured circles on to its faces. If you have difficulty matching the colours of the ribbons and the circles, use white ribbon and circles and colour them to match with felt-tipped pens.

HOW TO PLAY

This game is ideal to play outdoors. Teams of three children compete against each other to make the longest line using four posts and three lengths. Each player in turn throws the monster colour dice from the plant pot shaker and picks out from the box the string with that colour ribbon. If a colour has already been selected the child should throw the dice again. As each string is picked, the trio of children loop it over the first post and then, at full stretch, the ring at the other end is put over the second post. The second string is looped over this pole too and stretched out to the third post, and so on. When the three strings are stretched out, the line they make is estimated and then measured in metres with the tape. Award one point for each metre and an extra five points if the estimate is within 5m. Then the strings are returned to the bag and the next team goes through the same procedure. The team with the most points wins.

TEACHER'S ROLE

Once you have established that the children know clearly what they are doing, introduce the idea of the perimeter of a triangle. This is really the same game, but the length is bent into a triangle. The first length is

WHAT YOU NEED

Six lengths of string (see 'Preparation'), 12 rings, a box or bucket, four games posts and bases or cricket stumps, a large play brick, a plant pot (as a shaker), six different-coloured circles of paper or thin card, six short lengths of ribbon the same colours as the circles, a tape measure,

A large playing space such as the hall.

measured out as before with two posts, but the second string is hooked over the first post too and then left until the third string is selected and hooked over the second post. The second and third strings are joined together by one child holding the free ring on the second string and another child holding the free ring on the third string and both of them walking in an arc until they meet. The third child in the team can then put a post through both the rings to give a triangle shape. Point out that the shape is a triangle and that all the sides are visible. Measure all the sides. The total distance round the edge is called the perimeter. Help the children to open out their triangle to show how these three side lengths add up to the perimeter. The team making the longest perimeter wins.

REFLECTIONS

TEACHING CONTENT

☆ Recognising reflective symmetry (SSM: 2c; S: B)
☆ Practising symmetrical shapes (SSM: 2c; S: B)

PREPARATION

Introduce this game by experimenting in the classroom with mirrors. Encourage the children to see everything is in 'reverse' in the mirror. Tell them to touch their right cheeks and see that it looks like their left cheeks are being touched. Ask them to write their names and see how they are shown in 'mirror' writing.

HOW TO PLAY

This is a knock-out competition in which the winner is the last player left 'in' at the end. It could involve the whole class. Basically, it is 'Simon says' in a mirror. Stand at the front of the class. Tell them to space themselves out around the hall. Whatever you do the children have to copy except that they are to be your reflections 'in the mirror'. Each child has to imitate your actions, but has to be aware that reflections show things the opposite way round. So if you move your right arm, the children have to move their left arms. The children will have become accustomed to automatically compensating for the apparent disparity between right and left when looking at someone like this, so this game should cause some amusement. Anyone moving the 'wrong' way sits down. In time the children themselves will look out for anyone who moves the wrong way and then pretends she didn't! As the number of players is reduced, you can complicate matters further by introducing turns, speeding up and, occasionally, facing the same way as the children (that is, with your back to them). Let the rest of the class who are 'out' act as referees. The child left standing at the end is the winner.

TEACHERS' ROLE

Back in the classroom, go on to activities which further demonstrate and develop reflections of a three-dimensional structure in four directions. For example: using building cubes, all the same size, build a simple structure. Then using card squares the same size as the cube faces, ask the children to lay out 'reflections' in all four directions. Take away the centre cubes without disturbing the squares. Ask some other children to reconstruct

the cubes using the reflections as guides. More permanent 'reflections' could be made using paper squares pasted on to sugar paper. Make a display under the collective title 'What buildings do these reflections show?' Once they have grasped the principle, encourage the children to make more complicated constructions.

BATTLESHAPES

TEACHING CONTENT

☆ Plotting location on a squared grid in response to verbal instructions (SSM: 3b; PM: B/C)
☆ Identifying features of 2-D and/or 3-D shapes (SSM: 2b; RS: B/D)

PREPARATION

Make ten or more large cards, big enough for the class to see, showing a range of two- and/or three-dimensional shapes. The shapes you choose will reflect your chosen learning objectives. They could be all polygons or quadrilaterals or the skeletal outlines or nets of three-dimensional shapes.

This game is played outside. Chalk a large grid on to the playground; for example, with three lettered columns A, B and C, and ten rows numbered from 1 to 10. Also, the children will need at least two strips of paper and a paper clip for each card, pencils and some coloured chalk.

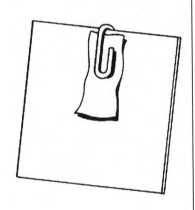

HOW TO PLAY

Split the class into two teams: A and B. Give Team A the shape cards and tell them to move well away from the other team. They must pick a square for each shape and write its position (as a letter and number) on a paper strip which is held on to the back of the card with a paper clip, face down so that any inadvertent mishandling will not reveal the location. Then Team A hold up the cards. Not all the children will have a card to hold necessarily, but everyone can take part in the question-and-answer session. In turn, each player in Team B picks a grid square and says its code, for example A1, B6 or C9. Each square called out has a

diagonal line chalked across it (by you or a member of Team A) and cannot be called again. If the square has a shape assigned to it, the player holding up that shape must also put it on the grid correctly. When everyone has had a go (one child may have two guesses if the numbers in the teams are uneven), Team B's total is counted. This may be one point for every shape on the grid, or points can be given according to the features of the shapes: number of sides, angles, edges, corners or faces. For example, a square would give four points for angles or sides. Finally the locations of the shapes which have not been guessed are revealed. If any location has been called and the shape not put down, then the score for that shape is doubled.

Then the teams swap roles. When recording Team A's guesses use a different-coloured chalk and draw a different diagonal.

TEACHER'S ROLE

You are very much the enabler of this game: keeping order, setting the goals and tallying the scores. Lead the discussion after the game through both grid locations and the characteristics of the chosen shapes. Which squares were not used by either team? What were the chances of calling out the reference of a square with a shape? (The number of squares divided by the number of shapes – 30 squares divided by ten shapes giving 3:1.) If the grid was twice as big, how many squares would it have? What would the chances be of getting a shape square then? How many angles/sides/corners are there altogether? How many did Team A get? How many more could they have got?

POLLY NAMES

TEACHING CONTENT

☆ Recognising polygons by their number of sides and angles (SSM: 2a; RS: D)
☆ Understanding of regular features of a polygon (SSM: 2b; RS: D)

PREPARATION

Make a monster dice using a play brick. Stick labels on to the faces and number them from 5 to 10 inclusive.

This game can be used to supplement the introduction of polygons. Talk about the regular and irregular shapes with which the children are familiar, drawing upon the children's knowledge of triangles and rectangles: What type of triangle is regular? How can we draw one? Demonstrate how to draw a base line and then use a pair of compasses, set to the base length, to draw an arc centred on each end. By joining the intersection point of the arcs and the ends of the base line, an equilateral triangle can be constructed. Go on to talk about shapes with more than four sides. Explain that they are called 'polygons'. Show the children examples of each of the following polygons and talk about the polygons' names and how the names were derived:

WHAT YOU NEED

Large 5–10 play brick dice (see 'Preparation'), plant-pot shaker.

Polygon means 'a plane, or flat, figure with more than four angles' from the Greek *polu-* (much or many) and *-gōnos* (angled).
Pentagon means a 'plane figure with five angles and five sides' from the Greek *pente* (five) and *-gōnos* (angled).
Hexagon means 'a plane figure with six angles and six sides' from the Greek *hex* (six) and *-gōnos* (angled).
Heptagon means 'a plane figure with seven angles and seven sides' from the Greek *hepta* (seven) and *-gōnos* (angled).
Octagon means a 'plane figure with eight angles and eight sides' from the Greek *oktō* (eight) and *-gōnos* (angled).
Nonagon means a 'plane figure with nine angles and nine sides' from the Latin *nonus* (ninth) and the Greek *-gōnos* (angled).
Decagon means a 'plane figure with ten angles and ten sides' from the Greek *deka* (ten) and *-gōnos* (angled).

HOW TO PLAY

This is a word identity game for two teams. A player from one team shakes the dice and asks a member of the opposing team to name the polygon with that number of sides or angles. Award one point for a correct answer, and a bonus point if anyone in the team can think of another word, not necessarily to do with maths, with the same prefix. Write these 'extra' words on the board. They cannot be used again. Then a member of the opposing team has a go as the questioner. Keep a tally of the points as the teams take turns. When everyone has had a go at asking and answering the questions, the team with the most points wins.

TEACHER'S ROLE

Most likely, you will not be surprised to see which children absorb the new words easily. However, the game will reinforce the class's awareness of polygons as a category of shape. Throughout the game encourage the questioners to vary their questions, otherwise they may tend to stick to the number of sides and forget about the angles. Keep referring to the unusual names.

You may like to go on to the geometric construction of regular polygons. The children should know that there are 360° in a circle. The children will need protractors, drawing compasses and calculators. Show them how to construct a pentagon as an example. Draw a circle. Divide 360 by 5 using a calculator. This gives 72°. Draw a line from the centre of the circle to the circumference (a radius) and measure and mark 72° from it. Draw another radius to this point. Then join the two points marked on the circumference. Repeat this four times to complete the pentagon. Measure each 72° from the previous radius. Discuss how this process can be used to draw polygons with more sides and encourage the children to try for themselves.

COPY CATS

TEACHING CONTENT

☆ Making and describing 3-D shapes (SSM: 2b; RS: B)
☆ Developing geometrical and positional language (SSM: 2a; RS: B)

HOW TO PLAY

Divide the group into two equal teams. Give each player a set of five different small three-dimensional shapes. Tell them to construct a tower or other arrangement using the five shapes and to make a record of it by drawing it on a piece of paper. This should be kept hidden from the other players. They should then dismantle the arrangement they have constructed, find a player from the opposite team and swap shape sets. Each player must then try to reconstruct his opponent's arrangement of shapes from verbal instructions given by the opponent. The player giving the instructions can use the paper and pencil record as a reminder, but must not use the *names* of shapes, only their properties, to describe them. A player who makes his opponent's shape correctly gains a point for his team. The finished shapes can be checked against the drawn record. At the end, each player should have made a shape and attempted to copy someone else's. The team with the most points at the end wins.

WHAT YOU NEED

A variety of small three-dimensional shapes, enough for each player to have a set of five different ones, paper and pencil for each player.

TEACHER'S ROLE

This is a game designed to develop the vocabulary children use to describe position and to talk about three-dimensional shapes. During the game, listen out for descriptions that are particularly good and, after the game, encourage those children to share their descriptions. Try to make the children aware of the various properties that could be described and emphasise that a good description will describe as many of these properties as possible.

GAME VARIATIONS

This game can be varied by changing the types of shapes used and the number of shapes the children have at their disposal for construction.

SHAPES SCAVENGER HUNT

WHAT YOU NEED

Paper, pencils.

TEACHING CONTENT

☆ Using geometrical properties and relationships to solve a problem (SSM: 1a; RS: B)
☆ Recognising features and properties of shapes and using these to classify shapes and solve problems (SSM: 2b; RS: C)

PREPARATION

For each team, you will need to prepare a list of items to be found. As far as possible, the lists should be equal in terms of the number of items and ease/difficulty of finding them. The lists *could* be identical, and the differing ways the children find solutions a point of discussion at the end. A sample list is shown in the illustration below.

HOW TO PLAY

This game uses the traditional 'scavenger hunt' format to focus on aspects of shape in the environment. Divide the group into teams (how many will depend on the size of the group) and give each team a list of things to be found. The lists can be infinitely varied and will depend on the ability level of the children, the environment included and, of course, on the amount of time available. Give the children a certain amount of time and then reconvene. The team gathering the most correct items wins.

TEACHER'S ROLE

You will need to ensure that the lists are appropriate to the children's ability. To make sure that the reading of the list doesn't present a problem, go over the list with each team before they set out. Gather the children back together after a suitable amount of time, and as a whole group discuss each team's solutions. Highlight any particularly inventive or sophisticated solutions and make sure all the children understand why they *are* solutions.

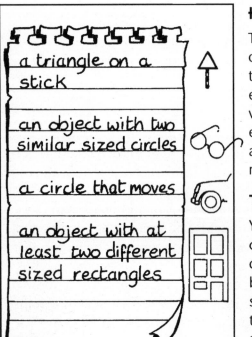

a triangle on a stick

an object with two similar sized circles

a circle that moves

an object with at least two different sized rectangles

MATHS GAMES

2
KEY STAGE TWO

Photocopiable games

TRAFFIC JAM

TEACHING CONTENT

☆ Estimating lengths in centimetres (SSM: 4a; ME: C)
☆ Measuring in centimetres to check estimates (SSM: 4a; ME: C)
☆ Adding and subtracting multiples of centimetres up to 1m
   (SSM: 4a; ME: C)

PREPARATION

Assembling the game: One full set of stand-up traffic cards (photocopiable pages 26 and 27) is needed. Copy them on to card. They can be coloured in before being assembled (as shown below). If you want the players to use the record strips, they will need a strip and a coloured pen each.
Introducing the game: Make a survey of the vehicles passing school. Talk about traffic jams: How can we avoid them? The children may suggest giant buses, or airships, or banning motor vehicles altogether!

HOW TO PLAY

This is a game for two or three players. The aim is to have the shortest traffic jam. Put all the stand-up traffic cards in the centre. Each player in turn rolls the dice and takes a vehicle/card with the same number. At the start of the game there will be more than one for each number. The players should try to select the shortest vehicle for the number thrown. If a number is thrown and all those vehicles have gone, the player does *not* have to take a vehicle and play passes on. When all the vehicles have been taken, the traffic jams are compared. The shortest queue wins.

TEACHER'S ROLE

Watch the players select the vehicles. Which children are really estimating the lengths and trying to select the shortest? After the game, discuss the 'best choice' for each throw. Ask the children to complete a record strip each. Tell them to measure each vehicle using a ruler and add all the lengths together. They can check their answers by measuring the whole traffic jam. Consider multiples of each vehicle: How long would five coaches be? How can we find the answer – by adding? Suppose there were 25 coaches, wouldn't that make a rather long adding 'sum'? How could we shorten it? (Multiplication by 10 [the length of the coach].)

GAME VARIATIONS

• Cut a 25cm strip of card for each player. They play as before, but now aim to make a traffic jam that fits the strip of card or is nearest in length to it when all the vehicles are gone. Ask the players to measure their jams and the strips with a ruler and develop a table of number bonds for 25.
• Make a traffic jam with a full set of cards. Measure it (102cm). (Take out a 2cm vehicle if you prefer 1m.) When a number is thrown, the player removes a similarly numbered vehicle from the jam, measures it and works out mentally how long the queue is now. This is checked by the group using a calculator. If the player is right, he can keep the vehicle. If he is wrong, then the vehicle is replaced. The new length is kept on the calculator display and will continue to decrease until all 18 (or 17) vehicles have been removed. The winner is the player with the most vehicles.

Stick and hold with a paper clip until the adhesive is dry.

HOW TO PLAY TRAFFIC JAM

For 2 or more players

YOU NEED: a full set of stand-up traffic cards, a dice and shaker.

❶ In turn, roll the dice and choose a vehicle with the same number. Put it at the back of your traffic jam.

Remember: the aim of the game is to have the shortest traffic jam.

❷ If all the traffic cards with a number have gone you do not have to take a vehicle. Play passes on to the next player.

❸ Play until all the vehicles have been claimed.

❹ Compare your traffic jams. The player with the *shortest* traffic jam is the winner.

motor bike			scooter		
horse and cart			lorry		
coach			minibus		
tractor and trailer			car and caravan		

STAND-UP TRAFFIC CARDS

bicycle			·
ambulance			⁞⁞⁞
breakdown truck			⁞⁞
container truck			⁞⁞
taxi			·
van			⁞⁞⁞
Land Rover			⁞⁞
car			·
handcart			⁞⁞⁞
horse			⁞⁞

27

RECORD SHEET FOR TRAFFIC JAM

Name

Shade in each vehicle you choose:

container truck	breakdown truck	ambulance
tractor and trailer	coach	horse and cart
car and caravan	minibus	lorry
horse	handcart	car	Land Rover	van	taxi
bicycle	m/bike	scooter	Total		cm	1st	2nd	3rd

Name

Shade in each vehicle you choose:

container truck	breakdown truck	ambulance
tractor and trailer	coach	horse and cart
car and caravan	minibus	lorry
horse	handcart	car	Land Rover	van	taxi
bicycle	m/bike	scooter	Total		cm	1st	2nd	3rd

Name

Shade in each vehicle you choose:

container truck	breakdown truck	ambulance
tractor and trailer	coach	horse and cart
car and caravan	minibus	lorry
horse	handcart	car	Land Rover	van	taxi
bicycle	m/bike	scooter	Total		cm	1st	2nd	3rd

WHAT YOU NEED

PHOTOCOPIABLE PAGES

Grid sheet 138, flower cards 31, 'How to play' sheet 30.

FOR CONSTRUCTION

Card, scissors, sticky labels, black marker pen, adhesive.

FOR PLAYING

Flower cards, letter/number grid, bag of 1–10 number cards, an A–F letter dice and shaker, 'How to play' sheet, an additional grid sheet (for recording) and a coloured pen for each player (optional).

PLANTING

TEACHING CONTENT

☆ Using letter/number coordinates to identify squares on a grid (SSM: 3b; PM: B)

PREPARATION

Assembling the game: Copy the grid on photocopiable page 138 of the Special Section and mount it on to cardboard. Laminate it if possible. The flower cards are best copied on to card. You will also need a bag of small cards numbered from 1 to 10 and an A to F letter dice. Stick labels on the faces of a regular dice and write on the letters with a black marker pen.

Introducing the game: Talk about gardens – the different flowers, their colours, the children's favourites and so on. Go on to discuss spring bulbs: Who has ever planted bulbs? What garden tool did you use? Impress upon the children that although bulbs look like onions they are not edible! Present this game as a competition between four rival gardeners who are planting out a display of spring-flowering bulbs.

HOW TO PLAY

Each player selects a set of flower cards. In turn, the players throw the letter dice and draw a number card from the bag. Together, these show a square where a (letter) column and a (number) row intersect and a flower card is placed there. If there is a flower in place on that square already, the player can do nothing and play passes on to the next player. The first 'gardener' to plant all her flowers wins. A paper copy of the grid will double as a group record sheet. The children can draw on the flowers as they place their cards, to practise further plotting locations on a grid.

TEACHER'S ROLE

During the game draw the players' attention to the number of flower cards they have left and whether there are any flowers of the same type next to each other. Remark that clumps of bulbs are much more effective than single ones. (This can become the basis of a game variation later.) Once the outcome of the game has been reached, the players could rearrange their flowers on the board to make a more satisfying garden.

GAME VARIATIONS

• Introduce points for getting flowers next to each other: one point for pairs, two points for threes and so on. This should encourage the children to look for patterns and to anticipate the best squares to pick.

• Play the game 'in reverse'. Let the children place the flowers one at a time and in turn on the board as they wish and then 'pick' them by choosing the coordinates. This emphasises wanting a particular square.

• Draw paths, fountains and so on, on to the board, in full squares, and reduce the number of flowers correspondingly: a square with a picture cannot have a flower card on it as well. You might like to enlarge the board, but then the children would need to draw out cards for both the columns and rows. Instead of identifying the squares, the children could pick coordinates for the intersections. Delete the letters and numbers and write them on the lines and 'plant' the flowers on the intersection points.

HOW TO PLAY PLANTING

For 2 to 4 players

YOU NEED: the letter/number grid, the flower cards, a letter dice and shaker and a bag of 1–10 number cards.

❶ Each choose a set of flower cards. Then sort out the playing order.

❷ Take turns to throw the dice for a letter and pick out a card for a number.

❸ Find the square with the same letter and number.

❹ If the square is empty, put a flower card on it. If it has a flower on it, play passes to the next player.

❺ The first player to 'plant' all his or her flowers wins.

FLOWER CARDS

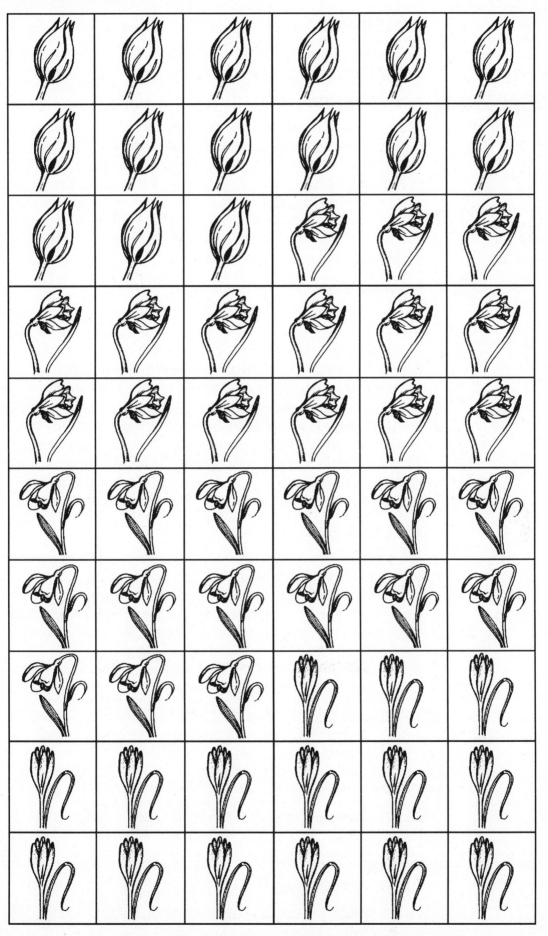

IN THE BALANCE

TEACHING CONTENT

☆ Practising weighing (SSM: 1e; ME: C)
☆ Combining weights to balance against a set weight (SSM: 4b; ME: B)

WHAT YOU NEED

PHOTOCOPIABLE PAGES
Mystery box sheet 34, 'How to play' and spinner sheet 33.
FOR CONSTRUCTION
Card, scissors, adhesive, black marker pen, weights such as marbles or washers, small sharp pencil.
FOR PLAYING
Six weighted 'mystery' boxes (see 'Preparation'), a dice and shaker, a weights spinner, a set of weights (2 × 1kg and 1 × 500g), a set of balance scales.

PREPARATION

Make six copies of the 'mystery' box net and mount them on to stout card. Identify each box with a dice number, written on to each face in the square provided. Construct the six boxes and fill them with objects such as marbles or washers. Do this away from the children. The boxes should weigh: 200g, 300g, 400g, 500g, 600g and 700g, but their weights should not correlate to the box numbers. When this is done, tape the lids down. You will also require a spinner showing 0.5kg, 1kg, 1.5kg and 2kg, a set of weights (2 × 1kg and 1 × 500g) and a set of balance scales.

HOW TO PLAY

This is a game for two or more players. First spin the spinner to determine the weight for the game. This weight is put on one pan of the balance scales. The mystery boxes are kept in the centre of play. Each player throws the dice and selects the box with that number. The box is put in the empty scale pan. If the scale pan goes down, the box is put back in the centre and play passes on to the next player. If the pan stays up, the box stays where it is, and play passes on to the next player who can put another box on as well. If the scale pan goes down, then *that* box only is taken off again. If a box is already on the scales and its number is thrown, nothing can be done and play passes on to the next player. If the scales balance, the player putting that box on is the winner.

TEACHER'S ROLE

This game will show how well the children handle a set of scales and their awareness of comparative weights. If no box or boxes balance the weight in the other scale pan there has been some error in setting up or playing the game. Check that the scales balance when there are no weights on them. Then check that the boxes are exact multiples of 100g and finally check the 1kg and 500g weights themselves.

After the game, get the children to draw up tables showing how the various weights can be achieved. For example:

0.5kg =	500g =	box ? + box ?, or box ? (where ? is a dice/box number)
		(200g + 300g, or 500g)
1kg =	1000g =	box ? + box ? + box ?, or + box ? + box ?
		(500g + 300g + 200g, or 600g + 400g)
1.5kg =	1500g =	box ? + box + box ?, or box ? + box + box ?
		(600g + 700g + 200g, or 500g + 600g + 400g)
2kg =	2000g =	box ? + box ? + box ? + box ?, or box + box ? + box ? + box ?
		(600g + 700g + 400g + 300g, or 200g + 500g + 600g + 700g)

See if the children can find out the weights in the boxes by a combination of boxes and the weights.

GAME VARIATIONS

Vary the weights to concentrate on either grams or kilograms, with all the boxes weighing below 1000g or over 1kg.

HOW TO PLAY IN THE BALANCE

For 2 or more players

YOU NEED: balance scales, weights spinner, 2 × 1kg and 1 × 500g weights, six mystery boxes, a dice and shaker.

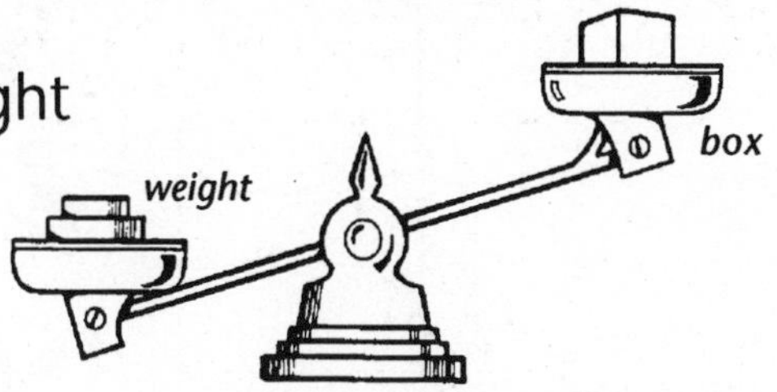

❶ Spin the spinner and put the weight shown in one pan of the scales.

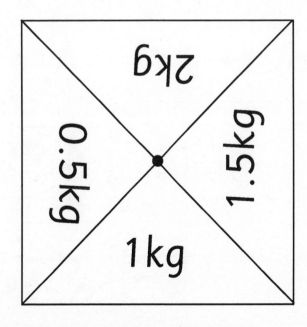

weight   *box*

❷ Sort out the playing order.

❸ In turn, throw the dice and put the same numbered box in the empty pan on the scales.

❹ IF the pan with the box goes down, the box is taken off.

IF the pan with the box stays up, another box can be put on it next go. If the pan goes down now, the last box is taken off.

IF the number of a box already on the pan is thrown, play passes on to the next player.

❺ When the scales balance, the player putting the last box on, is the winner.

WEIGHTS SPINNER

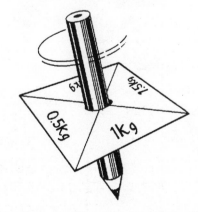

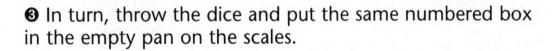

MYSTERY BOXES

x6

glue

glue

Print a dice number into the empty square on each face.

Fill with required weight. Then hold lid closed with sticky tape.

glue

glue

glue

glue

REQUIRED WEIGHTS

200g
300g
400g
500g
600g
700g

MEASURES MAT

TEACHING CONTENT

☆ Practising using measurement in real-life contexts (SSM: 1e; ME: C)
☆ Choosing appropriate standard units of length, mass, capacity and time (SSM: 4a; ME: C; and T: C)
☆ Choosing appropriate measuring instruments (SSM: 4b; ME: C)

PREPARATION

Mount the two halves of the measures mat on an A3 board or on two A4 sheets of card which can be held together with wide tape and folded like a chessboard. There are two different versions of this game which each require two different dice. The first version concentrates on measuring instruments; the second on standard units of measurement. Before assembling the dice, check that the measuring instruments are ones with which the children are familiar. If necessary, delete and replace an unfamiliar one with a similar, but better known example. The dice nets can be copied on to card and, once assembled, stuffed with crumpled paper to provide support, or the faces can be mounted on to play bricks, which would be sturdier.

HOW TO PLAY

The rules of the game are the same for both versions. Give the players either the two measuring devices dice or the two units of measurement dice. Each of the two to four players needs a set of eight same-coloured counters. If there are only two players, they may each have two sets of counters (16). In turn, the players have to choose which of the two dice they are going to throw for each move. The picture thrown has to be matched to a measuring task on the board. It must be a sensible choice. If anyone disagrees with the player's choice, then you may have to arbitrate. If it is agreed, the player puts one of her counters on the square. If no suitable task on a free square can be found, play passes on to the next player. There can only be one counter on each task. The first player to put down all her counters on the mat wins.

TEACHER'S ROLE

Naturally, you must decide which version of the game is going to be played. Initially you may have to referee, judging the case for and against the match of each instrument or task. This game lends itself to discussion as to why this measuring device or that unit matches a particular square. Throughout the game, ask the players to elaborate on their choices.

GAME VARIATIONS

• The board can be extended by adding additional tasks and the range of instruments and units can be varied to give more choices of dice.
• Instead of a matching game, the measures mat can be adapted into a race. Draw arrows on to the board as shown opposite. In this game each player has a different-coloured counter and can only move round the board when the dice picture that is thrown matches that on the next square.

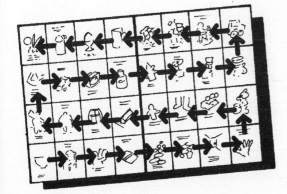

WHAT YOU NEED

PHOTOCOPIABLE PAGES
Game board sheets 38 and 39, dice nets sheet 37, 'How to play' sheet 36.

FOR CONSTRUCTION
1 × A3 or 2 × A4 sheets of card, adhesive, wide sticky tape for A4 version of board, scissors, paper clips, paper.

FOR PLAYING
A3 'Measures mat' game board, 8 counters of the same colour or 8 similar coins for each player, two measures dice of your choice and shaker.

HOW TO PLAY MEASURES MAT

For 2 to 4 players

YOU NEED: two measures dice and shaker, measures mat and a set of 8 same-coloured counters for each player.

❶ Put the counters in piles near each corner of the mat. Choose a colour. If there are only two players you may each pick two colours or have 16 same-coloured counters each.

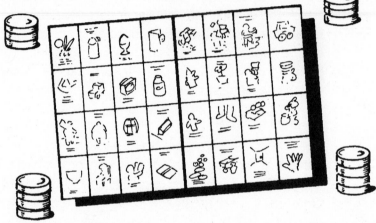

❷ Take turns. At each turn, before throwing the dice, you must choose which one to use. Then throw the dice.

❸ Match the picture or word thrown to a measuring task on the mat. It has to be the best measuring device/unit for the job.

❹ If one can be found, that does not have a counter on it already, you can put your counters on that task. If no free matching task can be found, the throw is wasted and play passes on to the next player.

❺ The game ends when all the tasks on the mat have a counter or when one player has so many counters on the mat, that no one can beat him or her.

❻ The player with the most counters on the mat wins.

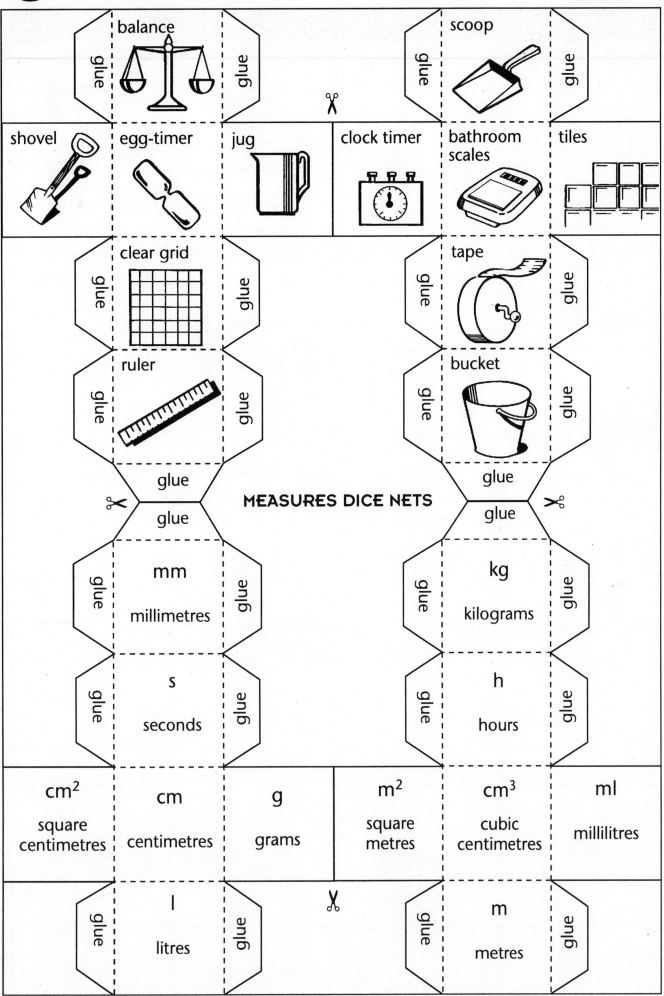

MEASURES DICE NETS

Weigh a cup of peas against a cup of feathers.

Fill a thermos flask.

Time boiling an egg.

Time a walk around the school.

Fill a toy lorry.

Time a film on TV.

Weigh a bottle of water.

Cover a floor.

Weigh a man.

Fill a water barrel.

Measure a line.

Fill a bowl.

Measure a chair.

Time a story.

Measure the cover of a book.

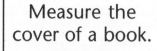

 Cover a patio.	Weigh ten house bricks. 	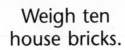 Fill a box with sand.	Time a car journey of 200km. 
 Measure a pencil.	Fill a plant pot with soil. 	 Cover a wall.	Weigh a pile of books. 
Time a 3km mini-marathon.	Measure a stride. 	Weigh three coins. 	Fill a sack. 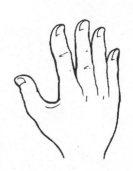
Weigh a bag of marbles against a bag of coins.	Fill a wheelbarrow. 	Measure a corridor. 	Measure the size of your hand.

TREES

TEACHING CONTENT

☆ Rotating through 30° angles of turn (SSM: 3c; A: D)
☆ Moving clockwise and anticlockwise (PM: B/C)

PREPARATION

Assembling the game: The two wheels (the base sheet 42 and mask sheet 43) should be mounted on to medium card. When they are dry, colour them in, giving the two-way arrows on the mask a distinctive colour. Fasten them together with a paper fastener (put sticky tape over the back). The record sheet is an integral part of the tree recognition on which the game is based. You will need a copy for each player.

Introducing the game: This game would be a useful follow-up to a science study of trees and shows the three main features of tree recognition – namely, the shape of the tree, its fruit or seeds and its leaf. Talk about the trees, leaves, fruit and seed shown on the wheel. If there are examples of these trees locally, highlight them to the children.

HOW TO PLAY

This game can be played either to practise clockwise/anticlockwise or angles of turn (in this case, 30° angles of turn – see 'Game variations'). The clockwise/anticlockwise game starts with the mask positioned to show the acorn. The players take turns to throw the dice and move the wheel: *clockwise* if the throw is an *odd* number (1, 3 or 5) or *anticlockwise* if the throw is an *even* number (2, 4 or 6). Each item they stop at is coloured in on their record sheets. Any player cannot colour in the same item twice, but several different players can colour in the same item. The first player to colour in a full set of tree shape, fruit and leaf wins.

TEACHER'S ROLE

During the game, note those children who find direction tricky. Now and then intervene to refresh their memories about clockwise – the direction of movement of the hands of a clock. A working analogue clock nearby may help; an old-fashioned alarm clock with a big, clear face is best.

GAME VARIATIONS

• Economise by using one record sheet for the whole group, with each player choosing a particular tree. The children can write their names above or below their tree. In this game, tree identification only counts if the player stops at items from his chosen tree.

• To practise just one direction, the arrows on the mask can be redrawn with the redundant points deleted and straightened. The players turn the wheel only the one way according to the dice throws.

• *Angles of turn*: If you want the game to reflect angles of turn, write 30° in small print under each picture (the cut-away area on the mask may need to be enlarged) and assemble the 30° angles of turn dice. The game is played by turning the wheel one way only (clockwise) with each segment counting as 30°. The dice dictates the number of 30° angles of turn per throw. The record sheet can be filled in as an individual or group effort.

WHAT YOU NEED

PHOTOCOPIABLE PAGES
Tree wheel base sheet 42, tree wheel mask sheet 43, record sheet 44, 'How to play' sheet 41.

FOR CONSTRUCTION
Card, scissors, adhesive, coloured pens or crayons, paper fastener, sticky tape.

FOR PLAYING
'Trees' wheel, a dice and shaker, a record sheet for each player, a 'How to play' sheet.

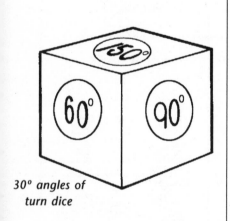

30° angles of turn dice

modified base for angles of turn game

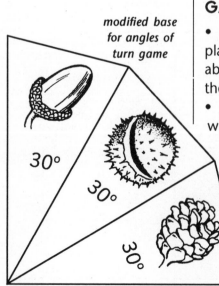

HOW TO PLAY TREES

For 2 to 4 players

YOU NEED: a record sheet for each player, the 'Trees' wheel, coloured pencils, a dice and shaker.

❶ Put the mask opening on the acorn.

❷ Take turns to throw the dice.

❸ Move the wheel round the same number of spaces as the number shown on the dice. The number also shows the direction:

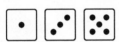 • Clockwise for odd numbers

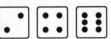 • Anticlockwise for even numbers

❹ Colour in on your record sheet each item the wheel stops at.

❺ The first player to get a full set of items for one tree – tree shape, leaf and fruit – wins.

ANGLES OF TURN DICE NET

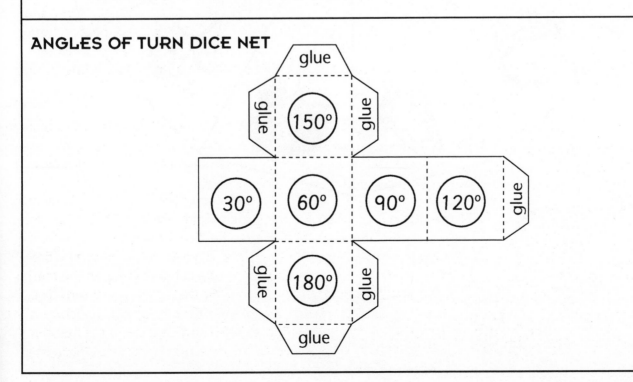

TREE BASEBOARD

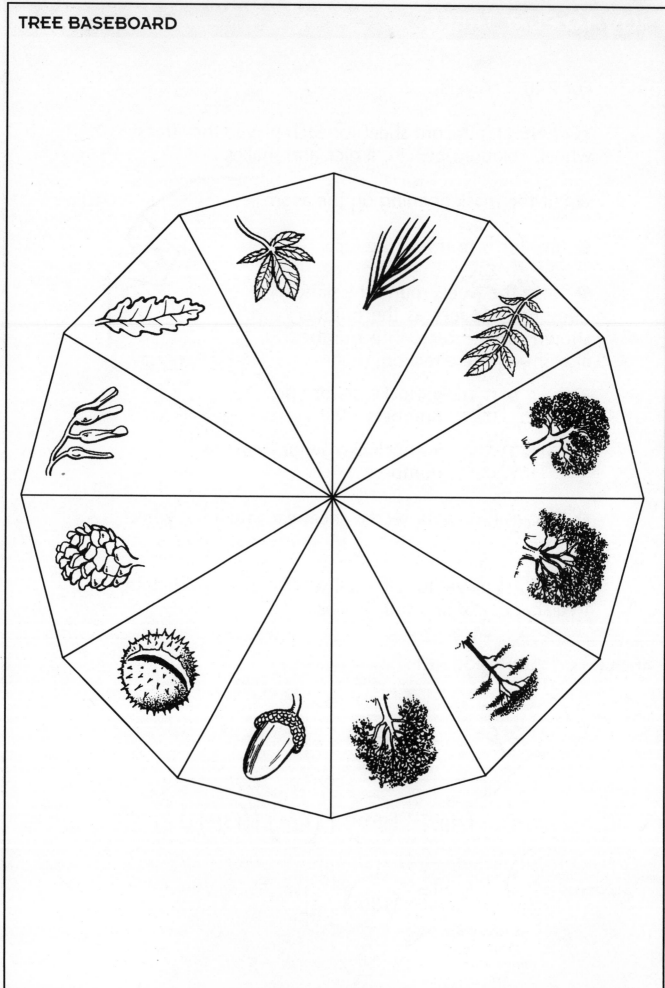

TREE MASK

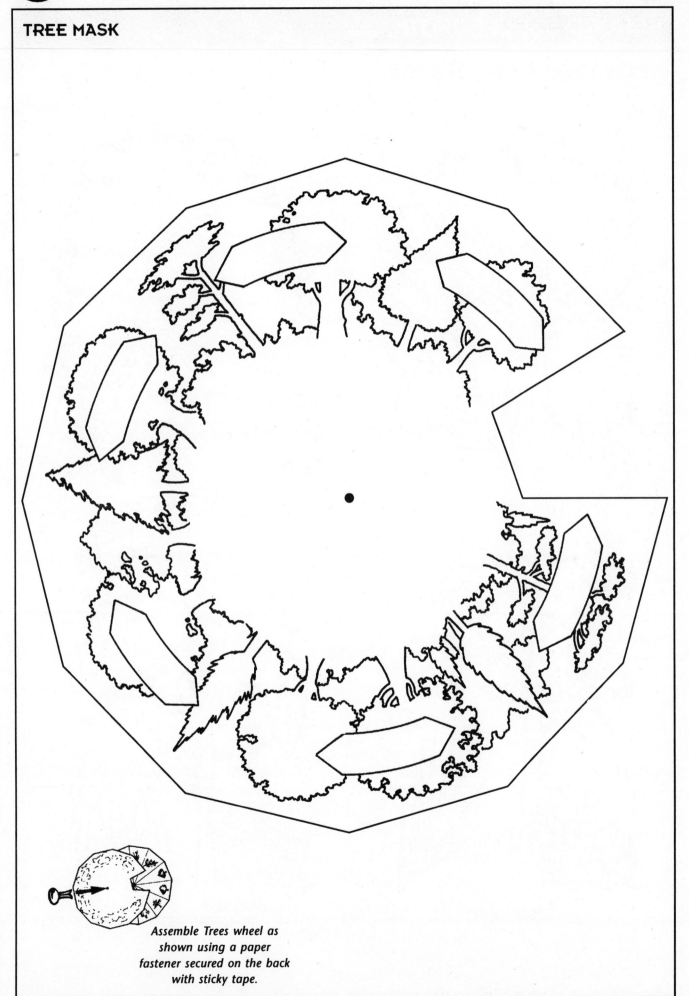

*Assemble Trees wheel as
shown using a paper
fastener secured on the back
with sticky tape.*

RECORD SHEET FOR TREES

Colour in each item the wheel stops at.

oak

horse chestnut

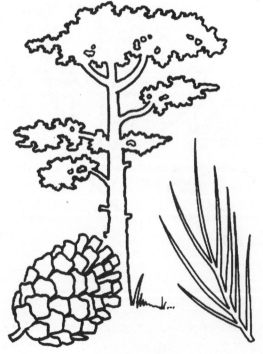

scots pine

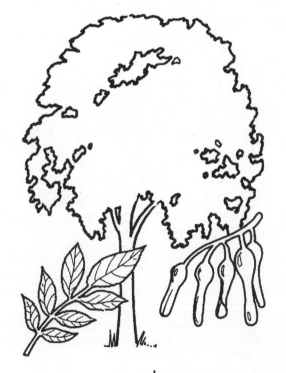

ash

TEMPERATURE CONTROL

TEACHING CONTENT

☆ Reading a scale with accuracy (plus and minus degrees Celsius) (SSM: 4b; ME: C)
☆ Understanding the importance of zero on a (thermometer) scale (SSM: 4b; ME: D)
☆ Deducing the intervals between the marked scale (SSM: 4b; ME: C)

PREPARATION

Assembling the game: This game is based on the movement of the 'liquid' in a model thermometer, the rise and fall in temperature being determined by the throw of the dice. To make the thermometer mount the 'board' (photocopiable page 48) on to thick card. When it is dry cut slots at 50°C and –50°C. Do not allow a child to do this, as it requires the use of either narrow-pointed scissors or a sharp craft knife. For the 'liquid' make a 'tongue' of card to pass through the thermometer. You can use the white strip on the left of the board mounted on to thin card and glued to the end of a similar-sized strip of red card. Alternatively, use a strip of white card twice the length and the same width as the left-hand strip and colour half in red. Finally, insert the tongue through the slots in the thermometer. A net is provided for a suitable dice on photocopiable page 47. However, as the thermometer scale is only in fives and tens, an ordinary play brick can be converted easily into a suitable dice with plus and minus numbers written on to sticky labels stuck on each face.

WHAT YOU NEED

PHOTOCOPIABLE PAGES
Thermometer sheet 48, 'How to play' sheet 47.

FOR CONSTRUCTION
Card, adhesive, scissors, craft knife, red marker pen or red card, play brick with sticky label on each face (optional).

FOR PLAYING
Model thermometer, temperature dice, 'How to play' sheet.

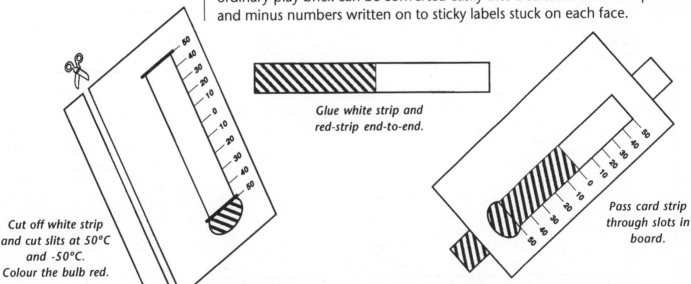

Cut off white strip and cut slits at 50°C and -50°C. Colour the bulb red.

Glue white strip and red-strip end-to-end.

Pass card strip through slots in board.

Introducing the game: You may wish to use this game to support a science topic about materials and their properties (expansion and contraction) or a geography topic concerning the weather, which can be extended into a practical maths demonstration of a block or line graph showing the children's own weather recordings. Use a real thermometer to record the weather every day. Each day nominate one of the children as the day's 'meteorologist' to make a note of the day's temperature, and move the model thermometer to show that temperature. An A3-sized thermometer, constructed as described previously, would be ideal for this activity. Draw the children's attention to the fact that the highest and lowest recorded UK temperatures are within the scale of the model thermometer, demonstrating that our (much maligned) weather is typical for a temperate country; that is, a country where extreme temperatures are rare. Take the opportunity to widen the children's understanding of how a thermometer works. Explain how the liquid in the thermometer tube (usually mercury or coloured spirit) expands in heat (when the temperature rises) and contracts in the cold (when the temperature falls). Explain, if necessary, that the teperature is read from the scale on the thermometer at the level of the surface of the liquid in the thermometer tube called the 'meniscus'. (This could be extended into a science investigation of surface tension.)

HOW TO PLAY

Any number of players can play this game, but if there are too many the game may be over before the last player gets a chance. Before starting, line up the division between the white and red halves of the thermometer tongue (the 'meniscus') with 0°C. In turn, each player throws the dice and moves the tongue up or down in line with the thermometer scale according to the throw of the dice. If a player moves the tongue on to 50°C or –50°C, the game ends in a draw and has to start all over again. The first player to get the thermometer back to 0°C is the winner.

TEACHER'S ROLE

You may like to explain how the various thermometer scales were arrived at. 'Centigrade' (old-fashioned, but still mentioned) just means a scale split up into 100 divisions between the temperature at which water boils and that at which it freezes. 'Celsius' is a centigrade thermometer scale named after Anders Celsius, a Swedish astronomer (1701–1744); and 'Fahrenheit' is a scale named after the German physicist, Gabriel Daniel Fahrenheit (1686–1736) who invented the *mercury* thermometer in 1714. When related to water temperatures, this has the awkward fixed points of 32° for water freezes to 212° for water boils. If possible, show the children real thermometers using both scales. Line up the temperatures at which water boils. Do the zeros align? 0°C matches with 32°F. Why is that? Which other places on the two scales match up?

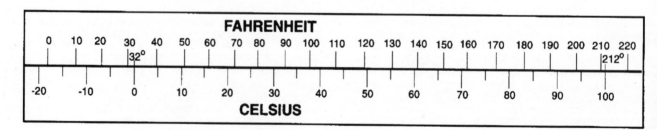

GAME VARIATION

Make a larger model thermometer by enlarging the board to A3 size. This would allow for the intermediate individual degree divisions to be drawn on to the scale. Let the players move by using an ordinary dice and tossing a plus or minus coin; that is a real coin with a sticky circle on each face marked plus or minus. As before, 50°C or –50°C is a draw and the first player back to 0°C is the winner.

HOW TO PLAY TEMPERATURE CONTROL

For 2 or more players

YOU NEED: the model thermometer, the temperature dice and shaker.

❶ Line up the thermometer with 0°C. Sort out the playing order.

❷ Take turns to throw the dice and move the top of the red 'liquid' in the thermometer up or down that many scale divisions.

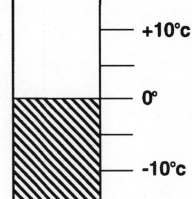

❸ If you move it to the 50°C or –50°C, it is too hot or cold to play! The game ends in a draw.

❹ The first player to move the thermometer back to 0°C wins the game.

TEMPERATURE CONTROL DICE NET

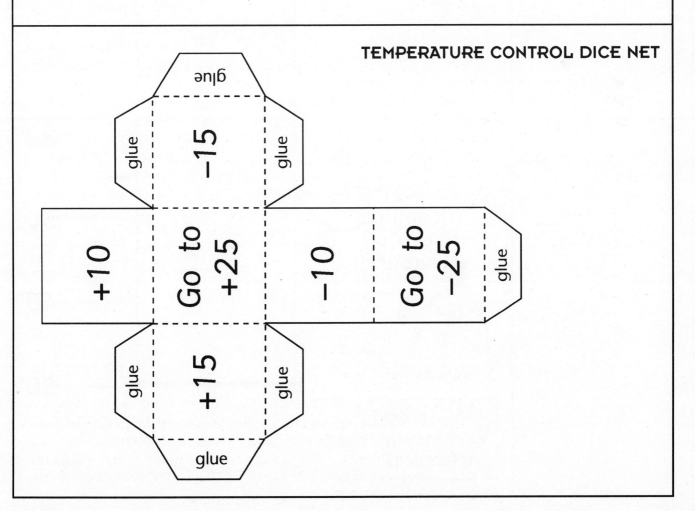

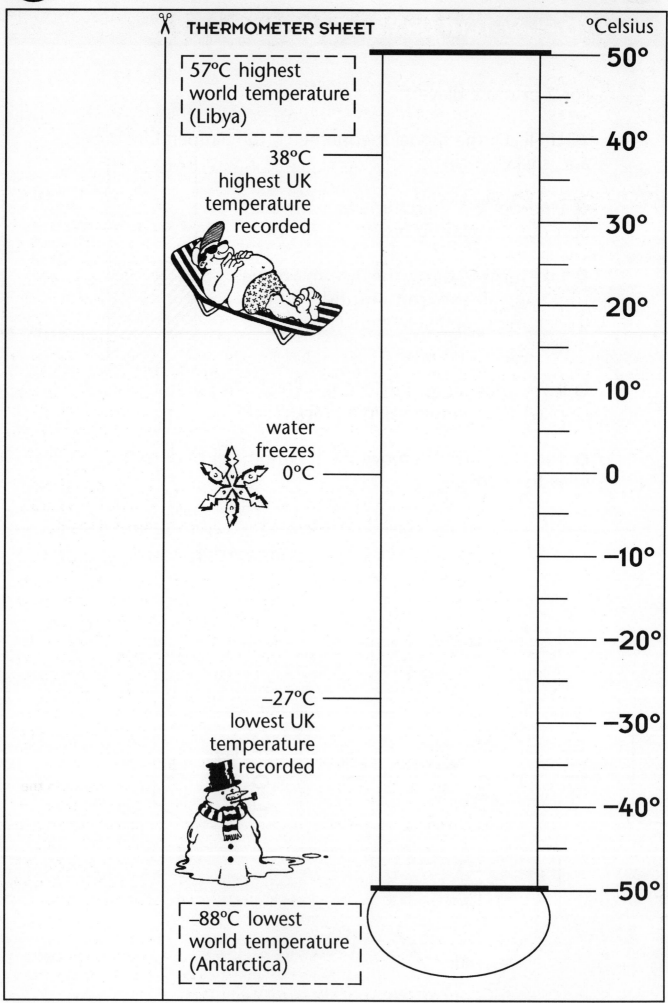

POLLY GONE

TEACHING CONTENT

★ Familiarisation with 'polygon' as a type of shape (SSM: 2a; RS: D)
★ Identifying polygons by the numbers of sides and angles
   (SSM: 2a; RS: D)
★ Learning how to construct a polygon (SSM: 1e; RS: E)

PREPARATION

Assembling the game: There are two types of 'Polly gone' cards provided for this game; one set with polygon shapes and the other with numbers of sides/angles. The game can be played with either one set or the other, or a mixture of both. You will need a full set of the chosen cards for each player. The polygon 'wheel' is best copied directly on to card. Attach the pointer with a paper fastener. Put a piece of sticky tape over the back of the fastener to stop it moving and to protect the children's fingers.

Introducing the game: Before the game, talk about 'polygons'. The name is derived from the Greek for 'many-angled'. Strictly speaking triangles and quadrilaterals are polygons, but these shapes have their own 'special names' which are used in preference. Also, the three- and four-sided shapes on the wheel are irregular. In these examples and at this stage, the children will be dealing only with *regular* polygons; that is, polygons with the same number of equal sides and equal angles. Their names are explained in the activity game 'Polly names', on page 20. Discuss the 'Polly gone' cards and ask the children to match the number and shape cards to reinforce the relationships of numbers of sides and angles.

HOW TO PLAY

Combine all the players' sets of 'Polly gone' cards and stack them, face up, in six piles; one for each type of polygon. In turn, each player throws the dice and moves the pointer on the polygon wheel clockwise according to the number thrown. If the pointer stops at a polygon, the player can take a 'Polly gone' card of the same type from the appropriate stack. If the player has an example of that card already, play goes on to the next player. Each player can have only one of each type of polygon. If the pointer stops at a shape that is not a polygon, play passes on to the next player. The first player to get a full set of six 'Polly gone' cards wins.

TEACHER'S ROLE

During the game, point out the differences between the shapes on the polygon wheel. After the game, draw the children's attention to the relationships between the number of sides and the number of angles: the more sides, the greater the number of angles and the nearer to a circle the shape becomes. Speculate with the children whether a polygon with a hundred sides would be nearer to a circle. Would it be possible to tell a polygon with thousands or even millions of sides apart from a circle?

GAME VARIATION

Accumulate points according to the number of sides/angles collected. The winner is the one with the most sides or angles. In this case, a player may have the same polygon more than once.

HOW TO PLAY POLLY GONE

For 2 or more players

YOU NEED: the polygon wheel, a set of 'Polly gone' cards for each player, a dice and shaker.

❶ Put the pointer on START.

❷ One by one, throw the dice and move the pointer clockwise on the number of spaces shown on the dice.

❸ If the pointer points to a polygon, you can take and keep a 'Polly gone' card showing the same number of sides. You may only have one of each card.

❹ If the pointer points to a shape which is not a polygon, play moves on to the next person.

❺ The first player to get a full set of six 'Polly gone' cards is the winner.

POLYGON WHEEL

START

POINTER

Fix the pointer in place with a paper fastener secured on the back with sticky tape.

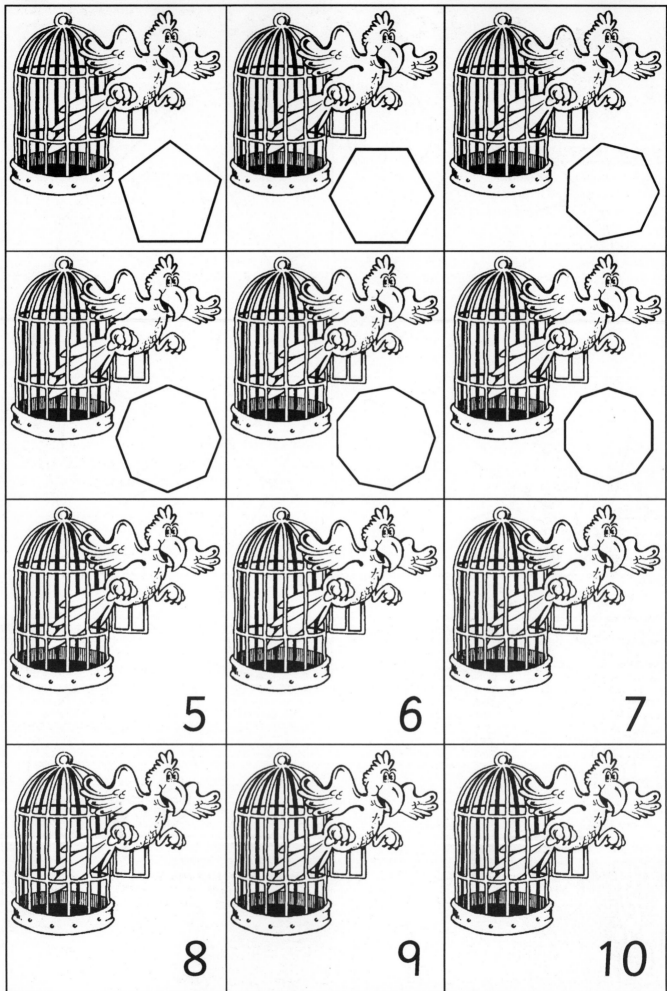

POLYGON CASTLE

TEACHING CONTENT

☆ Recognising polygons by overall shape, name, number of sides and angles (SSM: 2a; RS: D)

PREPARATION

The board for this game is assembled from four copies of the layout, mounted at right angles to each other on to a thick card baseboard. The 'castle' centre piece (given on sheet 56) is made from two halves stuck together. Hold the castle together with paper clips until the adhesive is dry. Then place it in the empty space in the middle of the board. A polygon dice can be made either by assembling the photocopiable dice net provided on page 54 and stuffing it with crumpled paper or by sticking the polygon shapes on to the faces of a plastic cube or play brick. Each player will also need a different-coloured counter.

HOW TO PLAY

Each player in turn throws the polygon dice and moves her counter forward to the next square related to the shape shown. The shape might be indicated by its outline, its name, its number of sides or its number of angles. To finish, all the players must throw a shape with ten angles to land on the drawbridge and can only gain entry to Polygon Castle by throwing the same shape as is given on its door (pentagon). The first to do so wins.

WHAT YOU NEED

PHOTOCOPIABLE PAGES
Game board sheet 55, 'How to play' sheet 54, centre piece and dice sheet 56.

FOR CONSTRUCTION
Thick card, scissors, adhesive, paper clips.

FOR PLAYING
Game board, polygon dice and shaker, a counter for each player.

TEACHER'S ROLE

During the game, interject with questions about current throws, and thereby underline the names and properties of the various polygons.

GAME VARIATIONS

• For a *much* longer game, the children could try to progress one square at a time by throwing the shapes in order: a pentagon, a hexagon and so on. As before, the first one to finish is the winner.

• Alternatively, and rather quicker, make two 5–10 dice by sticking labels to the faces of two play bricks and writing on the numbers. Again the players must progress one shape square at a time, but by throwing both dice together the child has two 'choices'. If a 'double' is thrown, whether the shape is wanted or not, that player gets another turn.

HOW TO PLAY POLYGON CASTLE

For 2 to 4 players

YOU NEED: the game board and castle centre piece, a polygon dice and shaker, a counter for each player.

❶ Choose a position on the board and sort out a playing order.

❷ Throw the dice and move forward to the next square on the board showing the same shape. No one can go backwards. The polygon can be known by its shape, its name, the number of sides or the number of angles.

❸ To finish all players must throw a shape with ten angles to land on the drawbridge and then one with five angles to enter Polygon Castle. The first player to do so wins.

POLYGON CASTLE GAME BOARD

x4

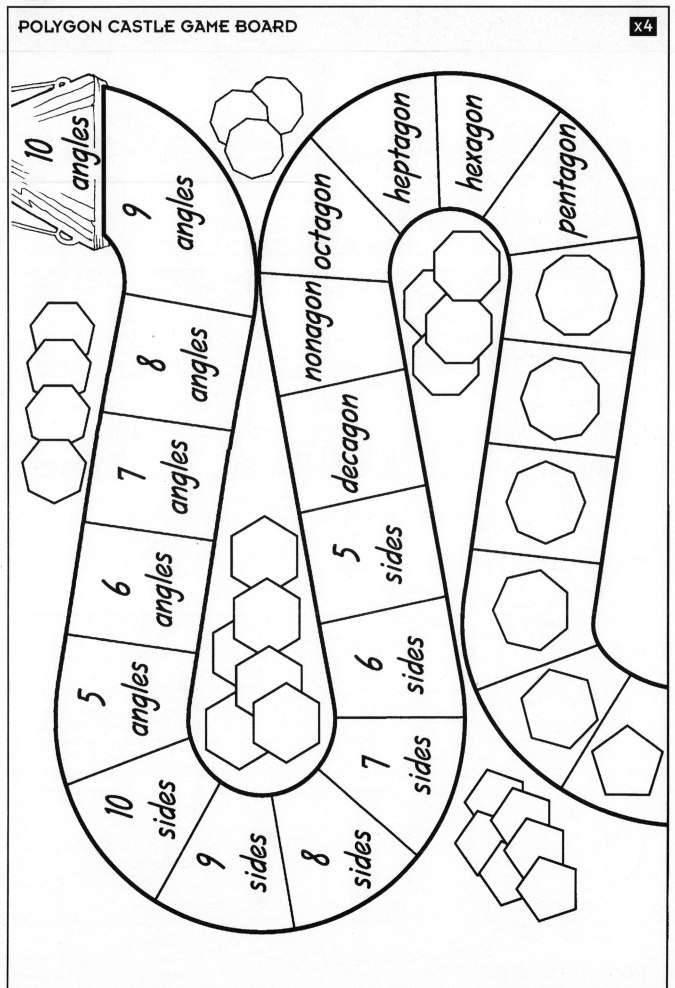

POLYGON CASTLE CENTRE PIECE

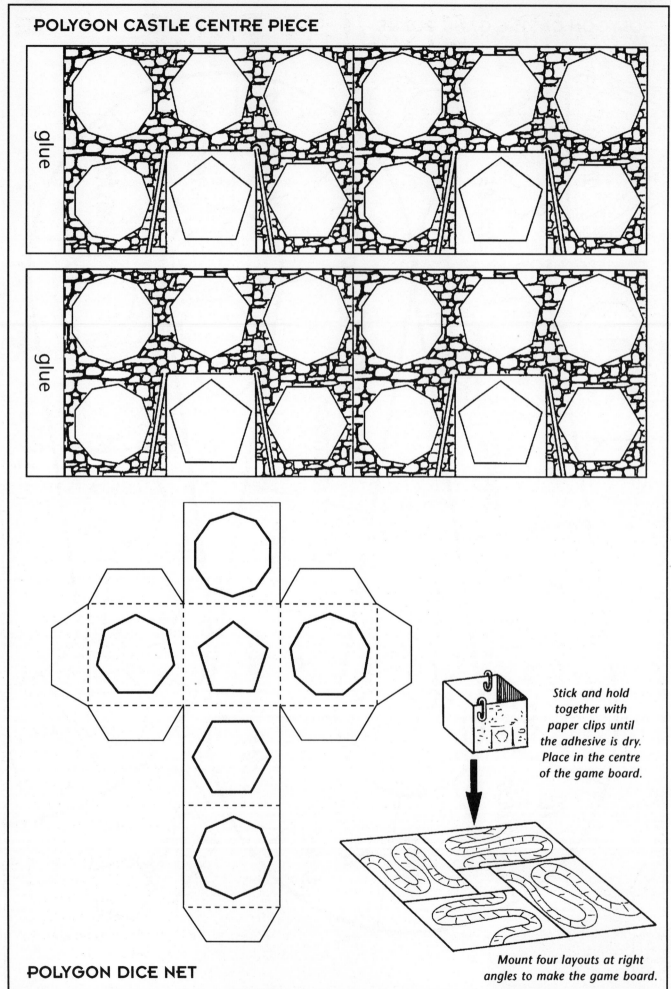

POLYGON DICE NET

Stick and hold together with paper clips until the adhesive is dry. Place in the centre of the game board.

Mount four layouts at right angles to make the game board.

GAMES

SNAIL'S PACE

TEACHING CONTENT

★ Extending the children's understanding of the perimeters of different shapes (SSM: 4c; PFS: D)

PREPARATION

This board game helps children to explore the shapes and lengths of the perimeters of four two-dimensional shapes. To make the board mount copies of the game board sheets on to a thick card base with the square and hexagon to the left. They can be mounted on to an A3 board or on to two A4 boards held together with wide sticky tape, so that they can be folded like a chessboard. Copy the snails (on photocopiable page 58) on to card and assemble them. Hold them together with paper clips while the adhesive dries. Four coloured counters could be used instead of the snails. The record strips (page 59) are an optional extra. If you choose to use them, you will need one for each player.

HOW TO PLAY

Each player chooses a shape on the board and a snail. The snails are put on their start squares. To move, each player throws the dice and moves that number of dots along the lines around his shape. An exact number must be thrown to finish. The first snail to go all round a shape wins. Play then stops and the positions are worked out according to the distances to be completed.

TEACHER'S ROLE

After the game, go through the various aspects of perimeters. You will get more from any question-and-answer session if the record strips are completed by marking the length of each side and how far the snails travelled. First, ask the players how far from the end their snails were. How far had they gone? (From this discussion they should deduce that all the shapes have the same number of dots.) How many sides did their shapes have? How long was each side? What is the relationship between the number of sides and the length of each side? (Since all the shapes have the same length perimeter, the fewer sides a shape has, the longer each individual side must be.) Compile a simple table of number sentences showing the number of sides and their lengths and the perimeter:

Triangle (3)   12 + 12 + 12 = 36 ...
Hexagon (6)   6 + 6 + 6 + 6 + 6 + 6 = 36

Throughout the discussion stress the word 'perimeter' and the names of the shapes: square, rectangle, hexagon and triangle.

The children's understanding may be extended by asking them to complete perimeter fact cards (as shown in the illustration opposite) for as many types of shape as they can find.

WHAT YOU NEED

PHOTOCOPIABLE PAGES

Game board sheets 60 and 61, playing pieces and 'How to play' sheet 58, record strips sheet 59 (optional).

FOR CONSTRUCTION

1 × A3 or 2 × A4 sheets of thick card, sticky tape (optional – for A4 board), thin card, scissors.

FOR PLAYING

Game board, a dice and shaker, a snail playing piece or counter for each player, a record strip for each player (optional).

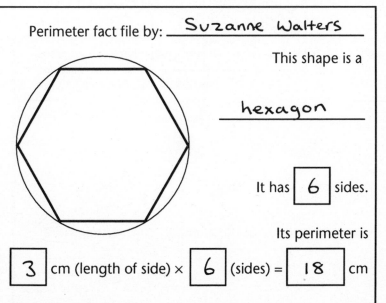

Perimeter fact file by: __Suzanne Walters__

This shape is a

__hexagon__

It has ⬚6 sides.

Its perimeter is

⬚3 cm (length of side) × ⬚6 (sides) = ⬚18 cm

HOW TO PLAY SNAIL'S PACE

For 2 to 4 players

YOU NEED: Snail's pace game board, a dice and shaker, a snail for each player.

❶ Choose a shape and put your snail on the start square.

❷ In turn, throw the dice and move your snail along the line.

❸ The first snail to go all round its shape wins.

❹ Stop play there and work out second, third and fourth positions from how far each snail has gone round its shape.

SNAIL'S PACE PLAYING PIECES

*Stick and hold together with
a paper clip until the
adhesive is dry.*

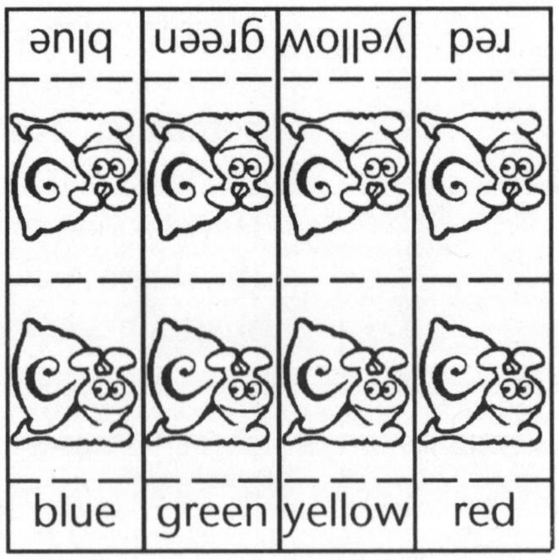

blue	green	yellow	red
blue	green	yellow	red

RECORD SHEET FOR SNAIL'S PACE

Name

My snail went ☐ cm

1st	2nd	3rd	4th

This line is half size.

Draw a cross at the end of each side.

Name

My snail went ☐ cm

1st	2nd	3rd	4th

This line is half size.

Draw a cross at the end of each side.

Name

My snail went ☐ cm

1st	2nd	3rd	4th

This line is half size.

Draw a cross at the end of each side.

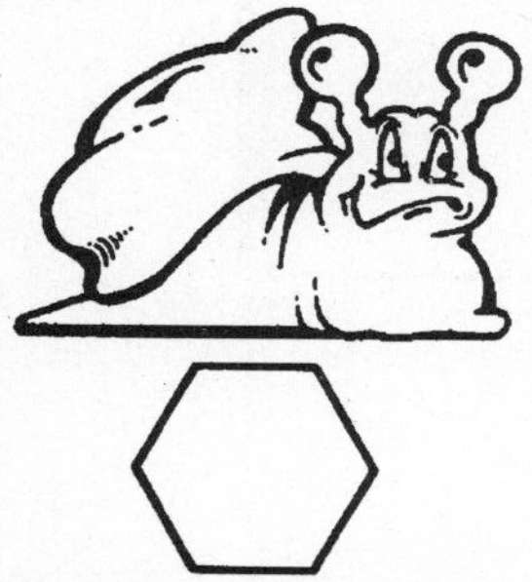

Name

My snail went ☐ cm

1st	2nd	3rd	4th

This line is half size.

Draw a cross at the end of each side.

SNAIL'S PACE GAME BOARD

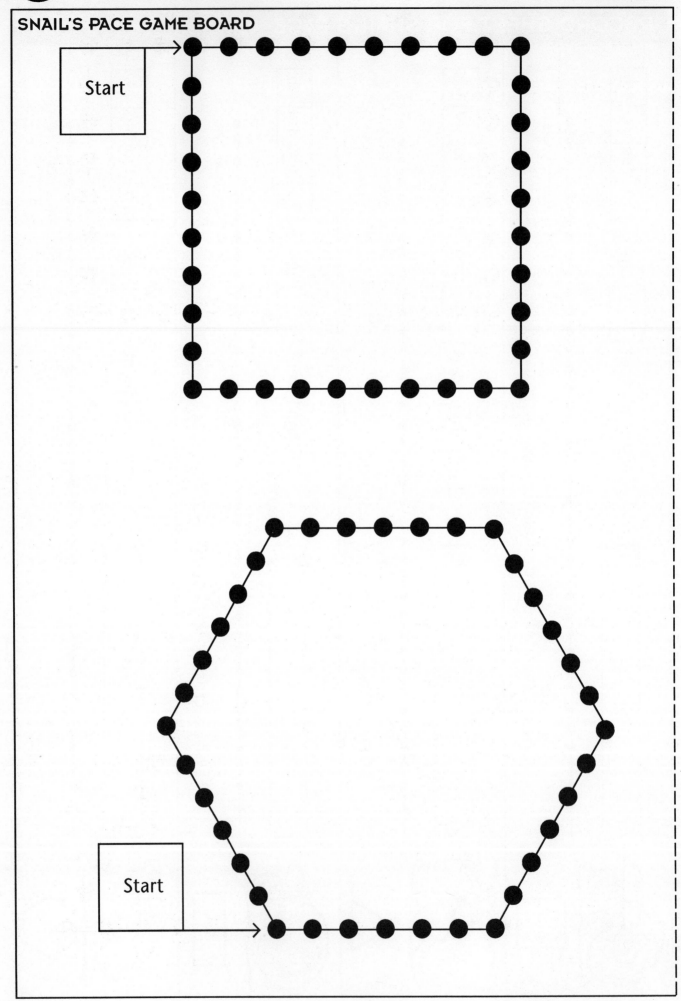

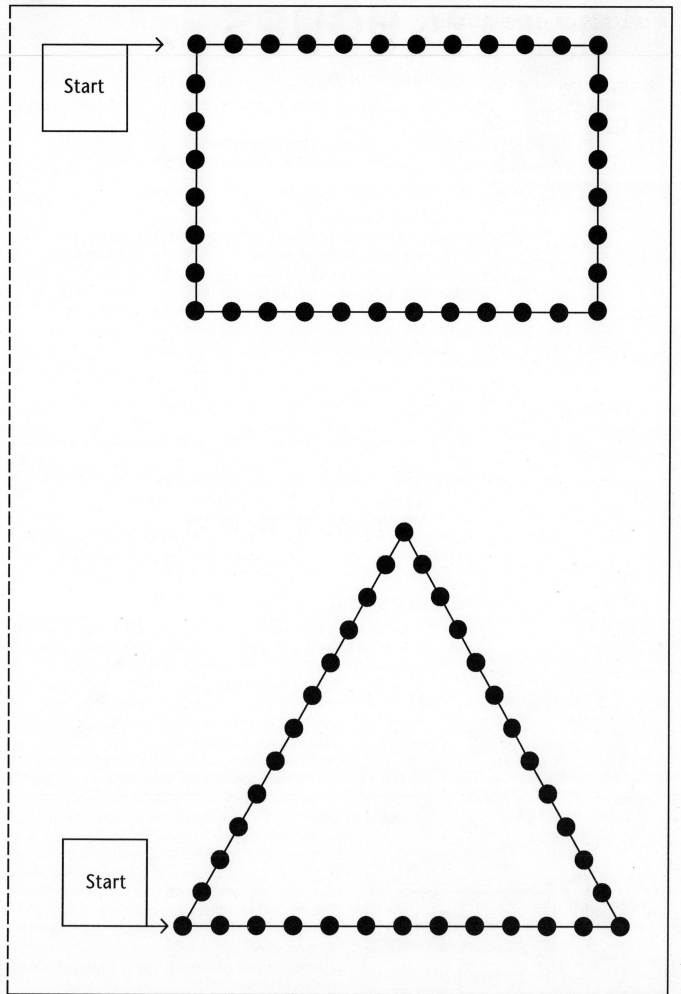

Start

Start

24 HOURS

WHAT YOU NEED

PHOTOCOPIABLE PAGES
Clock tiles sheet 64, 'How to play' sheet 63.

FOR CONSTRUCTION
Thin card, paste, scissors.

FOR PLAYING
Opaque bag, a set of tiles showing analogue and digital clock times.

TEACHING CONTENT

☆ Matching analogue and digital methods of showing the time of day (SSM: 1b; T: C/D)
☆ Practising using the 24 hour clock (N: 4a; T: D)
☆ Equating 12 hour and 24 hour clocks (N: 4a; T: D)

PREPARATION

Assembling the game: In this game the players are required to match pairs of tiles showing digital and analogue clocks. The sheet of tiles should be copied directly or mounted on to thin card and cut into individual tiles. These should be kept in an opaque bag.

Introducing the game: It is expected that the players will have had experience of digital displays and analogue clocks before playing this game. Also, they should be familiar with the 24 hour 'clock' system of counting time.

HOW TO PLAY

The tiles are shaken in the bag. The first player takes out four cards and turns them face up in the centre of play. If the times shown of any two cards match, the player keeps them, for example, an analogue 3 o'clock and a digital 03:00. If none match, the cards stay where they are and the next player takes out one card and turns it face up with the others. If there is a match now, that player can keep the matching cards. The players keep taking out one tile at a time, keeping any pairs when they occur. Unclaimed tiles remain on the table. If all the tiles on the table are paired before the bag is empty, the next player takes out four tiles. When all the tiles have been claimed, the player with the most pairs wins.

TEACHER'S ROLE

After the game, discuss how and where the 24 hour clock is used: videos and timetables are obvious examples. Use the tiles as flash cards. How quickly can the children recognise analogue times? When a digital example is flashed up, ask them the analogue time. Revise their knowledge of am and pm: What do they mean? *'Ante meridiem'* means 'before noon' and *'post meridiem'* means 'after noon'. 'Meridian', the English word for 'of noon', is derived from the Latin *meridies*, meaning midday.

Ask the children to draw cartoon-strip style pictures of a simple sequential story, for example a car journey. They could draw a family getting into a car, then filling up with petrol, another of the family on the beach and, finally, one of the car going the other way. Encourage the children to caption their pictures. Then ask them to pick four '24 hours' tiles with times that could match the journey. How long did each story take? How much time have the children allowed between each event/picture? Does that seem 'about right'?

14·05

17·00

HOW TO PLAY 24 HOURS

For 2 or more players

YOU NEED: an opaque bag of clock tiles.

❶ Shake the bag and sort out the order of play.

❷ The first player should take our four tiles and place them face up in the centre. If any two times match that player can keep them.

❸ If none match, the cards stay where they are and the next player takes out one card and turns it face up with the others. If a pair match, the player may keep them.

❹ Keep taking out one tile at a time in turn and keep any pairs of cards you spot.

❺ When all the tiles have been claimed, the player with the most pairs wins.

CLOCK TILES

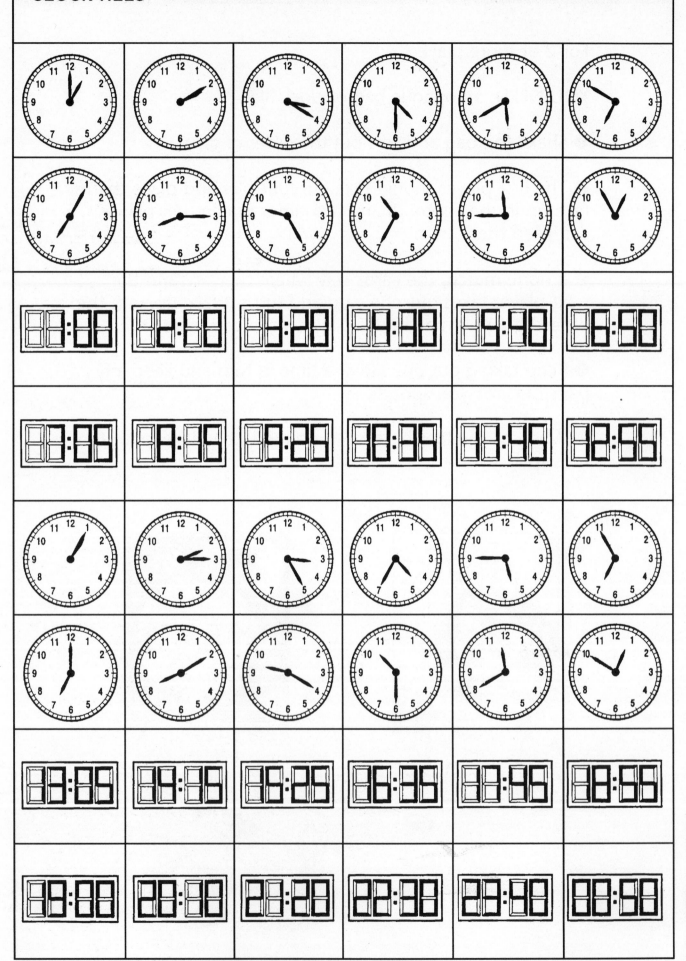

MYSELF

TEACHING CONTENT

☆ Producing a measurement data file about myself (SSM: 1e; ME: D)
☆ Comparing data about myself with data about other living creatures (SSM: 4a; ME: D)

WHAT YOU NEED

PHOTOCOPIABLE PAGES
Data file sheet 66, 'Myself and ...' sheets 67 and 68.

FOR CONSTRUCTION
No special equipment required.

FOR PLAYING
A data file and two 'Myself and ...' sheets, a pencil and calculator for each child, bathroom scales, tape measures, stop-watches or clock timers, chalk.

PREPARATION

Assembling the game: Unlike most of the games in this book, the competitive element is not so apparent. It is left in the hands of the teacher. Each child will need a copy of the three data sheets, a pencil and a calculator. Also, they will need a variety of measuring devices available, such as bathroom scales, tape measures and stop-watches or clock timers.

Introducing the game: Ask the children to fill in a data file sheet each about themselves. This can be a class activity done in groups, or a small group or paired activity carried out over a period of time such as a week. This process of data collection will help to improve the children's measuring skills. Demonstrate how to read and record each measurement. If necessary, show the children how to calculate their speed in metres per hour. They should time themselves running between two chalk marks and then multiply up the result. Taking an average of three or four timings would be more accurate. Some children may be very sensitive and self-concious about issues of body size. However, the results of the data collection are compared with totally different sets of criteria to get away from the usual classroom comparison of like with like, child with child.

HOW TO PLAY

The two activity sheets 'Myself and the animals' and 'Myself and the insects' are completed by each child using the information collected on his data file sheet. Both require simple use of the calculator. The sheets can be coloured in.

The teacher will determine the competitive level of this game/activity. There could be questions such as: Who is the nearest to the height of a giraffe? Who is furthest away from the weight of an elephant? The game lends itself particularly to name strips arranged in ascending and descending order. Being top and/or bottom of the lists can be seen as being a 'winner', since physical characteristics are, on the whole, as much to do with chance as the throw of a dice in a board game.

TEACHER'S ROLE

At the completion of the data files, go through them with the whole class. Speed, in particular, may need explanation and could be taken to kilometres per hour by dividing the metres per hour by 1000.

GAME VARIATION

Having got the idea of comparison with animals, the children should be encouraged to find comparative measurements concerning a wider range of things. These do not necessarily have to be living. Would all the class be as tall as Nelson's Column in London (approx. 52m), for example?

DATA FILE ABOUT MYSELF

Name _____

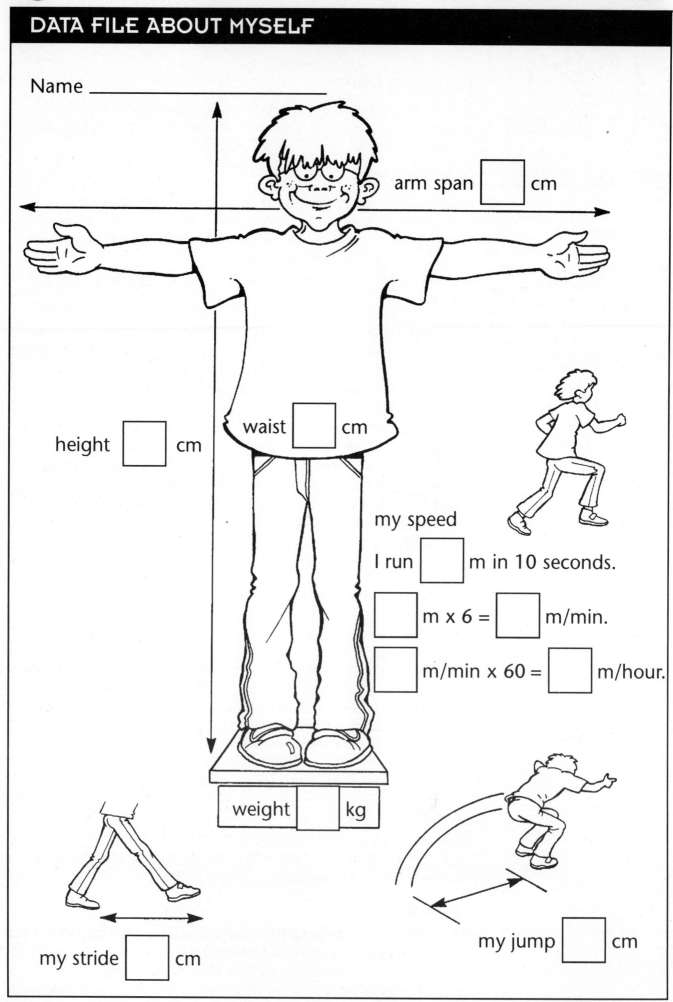

arm span [ ] cm

waist [ ] cm

height [ ] cm

my speed

I run [ ] m in 10 seconds.

[ ] m x 6 = [ ] m/min.

[ ] m/min x 60 = [ ] m/hour.

weight [ ] kg

my stride [ ] cm

my jump [ ] cm

MYSELF AND THE ANIMALS

I am [ ] times shorter than the giraffe.

animal's size ÷ my size

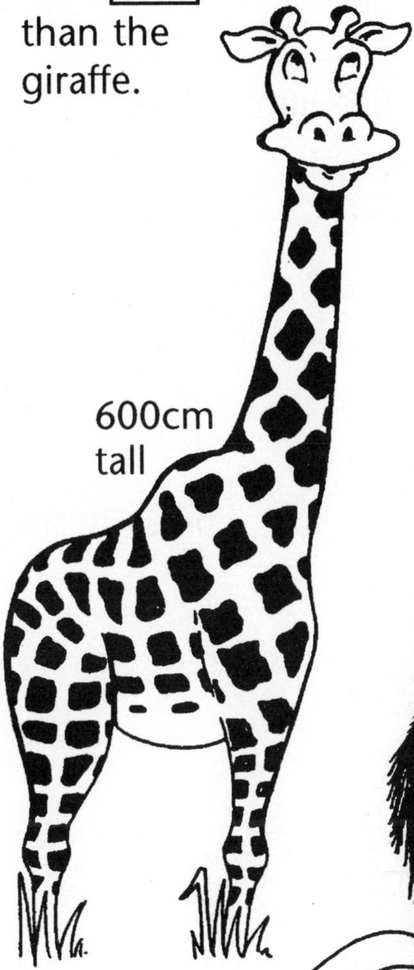

600cm tall

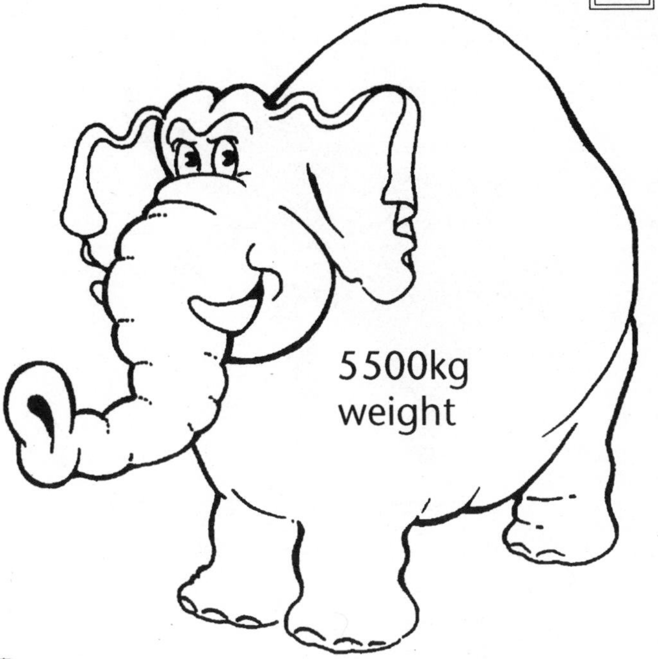

5500kg weight

I am [ ] times lighter than the elephant.

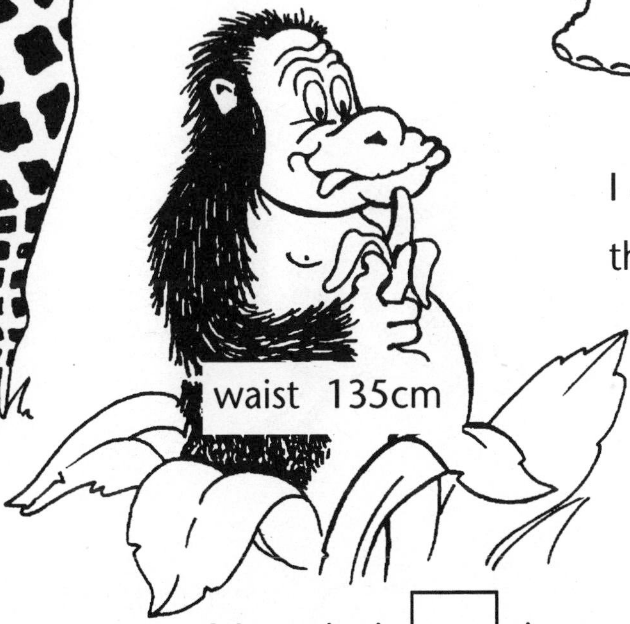

waist 135cm

My waist is [ ] times narrower than the gorilla's.

jumps 1200cm

speed 100000m/h

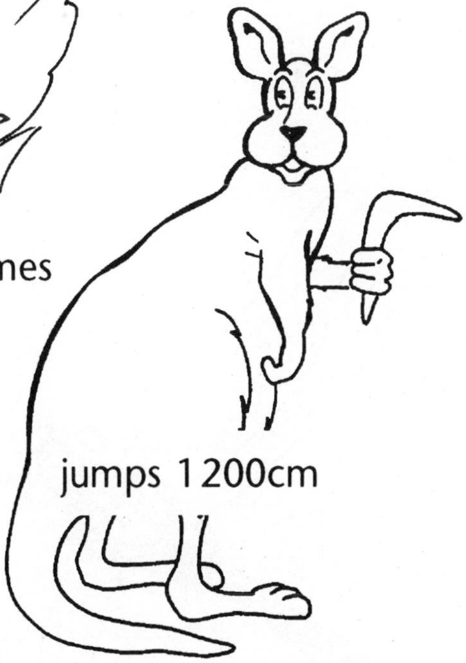

I am [ ] times slower than the cheetah.

My jump is [ ] times shorter than the kangaroo's.

MYSELF AND THE INSECTS

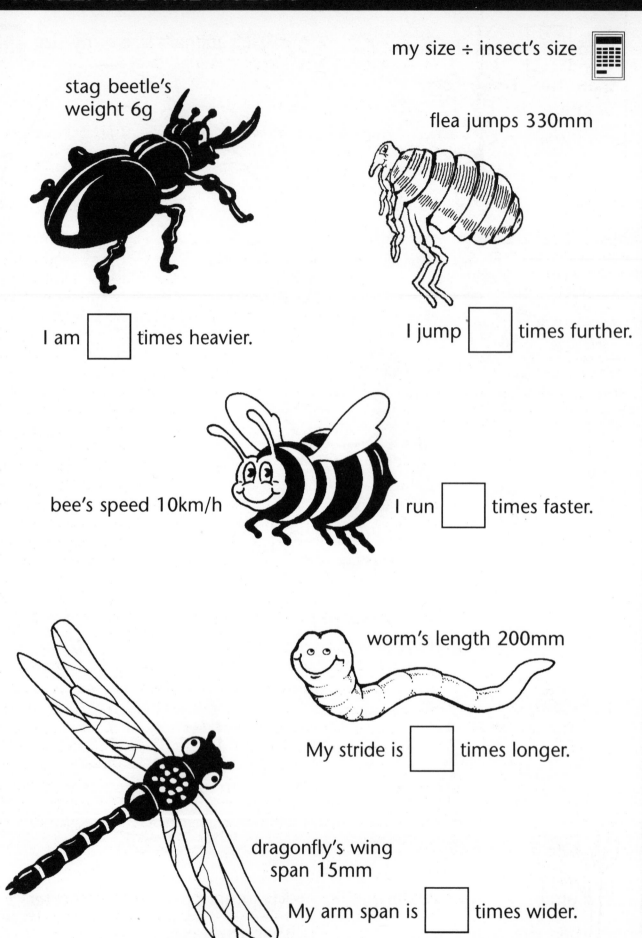

my size ÷ insect's size

stag beetle's weight 6g

flea jumps 330mm

I am ☐ times heavier.

I jump ☐ times further.

bee's speed 10km/h

I run ☐ times faster.

worm's length 200mm

My stride is ☐ times longer.

dragonfly's wing span 15mm

My arm span is ☐ times wider.

THE LION AND THE ROSE

TEACHING CONTENT

☆ Providing a practical context in which to estimate when one or two halves of a square are needed to fit an area (SSM: 1c; ME: C)
☆ Using non-standard units (squares and triangles [half squares]) to measure area (SSM: 4a; ME: C)

WHAT YOU NEED

PHOTOCOPIABLE PAGES
Game board sheet 72, tiles sheet 73, 'How to play' and centre piece sheet 71.
FOR CONSTRUCTION
Card, scissors, adhesive, coloured crayons or pens.
FOR PLAYING
Game board, a set of 'rose' tiles and a set of 'lion' tiles for each player, a dice and a shaker.

PREPARATION

Assembling the game: The game board is composed of four copies of the room layout (photocopiable page 72), positioned at right angles to each other around the centre piece. Make sure that the centre piece exits line up with those on the room layouts. The board is best coloured and laminated. Alternatively, mount it on to a thick card baseboard. Copy the tiles sheet on to card for each player. Colour the 'lion' tiles in yellow and the 'rose' tiles in red and cut up the sets.

Introducing the game: This game is based on tiling a floor. Through it, area can be measured practically using non-standard units and the relationship between the square tiles and the triangles (halves of squares) can be demonstrated. To help the children to use the triangles correctly, they can only be used on the yellow 'lion' floor. The two floors show the heraldic symbols of the lion and the Tudor rose. You could introduce this game as an escape adventure where the children have to cover alarmed floors with tiles in order to escape their unnamed captors. Or, this game could be linked to the Key Stage 2 history core unit: Life in Tudor times. Talk about the art and architecture of the period. Discuss the symbol of the Tudor rose. The children could imagine that they are helping to build a royal residence with ornate mosaic floors. The first builder to complete both floors will receive a 'royal' gift – at the discretion of the teacher!

HOW TO PLAY

Give each player a set of yellow 'lion' and a set of red 'rose' tiles. The players take turns to throw the dice and lay down that number of tiles on their layouts; roughly in position to begin with, as the pictures will not be clear. As the children put down more tiles, they can be rearranged to make the pictures. Five and six do not count. If either are thrown, the player can do nothing and play passes on to the next player. Encourage the children to finish one floor before starting the other. The first player to cover the two floors and complete the pictures is the winner. Stop the game there and work out the positions from the area of floor each player has left to cover (find this out by counting uncovered squares).

TEACHER'S ROLE

During the game, note which children seem to know when to use the triangular half squares. Following the game, ask how many squares each player has covered and how many are left to be covered, taking into account the half squares.

If they have problems, show them how two triangles make a square. How many squares does the whole floor need? Do you know any places covered in floor tiles? Are they square ones like these?

GAME VARIATION

Increase the number of squares by using 2 × 2cm squares (quarter each square shown on the board). In this case, the half square (triangular) spaces in the octagonal room would be of special interest. When using 4 × 4cm squares they require one half square, but when using 2 × 2cm squares they need two half squares and a full square. Compare the results of the 4 × 4cm game and the 2 × 2cm game.

EXTENSION

☆ Beginning to use metric units (SSM: 4a; ME: C)
☆ Using game pieces (square tiles) as scale representations of a square metre (1 tile = 1m²) to measure area (SSM: 4c; ME: E)
☆ Using easily handled fractions of a unit (triangle = half square) (SSM: 4a; ME: B/C)
☆ Using abbreviations 'm²' and/or 'cm²' (SSM: 4a; ME: B/C)

This extension introduces the concepts of the square metre and of scale, as each centimetre on the board represents one metre. Initially, show the children a square metre of newspaper and a square centimetre of paper. Explain how, in the game, each square centimetre now stands for an area the size of the newspaper (1m²).

There are two possible versions of this extension. The game can be played as before, but concentrating on expressing the results as square metres. Each player will need a record sheet (photocopiable page 74) and records the covering of the two floors by colouring in the same spaces as the tiles they have put in place. When one player has finished, stop the game and tell everyone to count their squares. Work out a finishing order. Bring out the conversion of centimetres to metres. Point out the heavy lines on the record sheet showing the 16 small squares in each square tile and the eight squares in each triangle. Let the children use rulers to answer questions such as: How many square metres have you completed? How many more do you need? How long is each side of each room? What is the perimeter of the 'rose' room? How far is it from the centre to the exit? Relate these measurements to similar ones in the classroom.

The second version concentrates on the plans of the rooms and is more abstract. The players will need coloured pens, two dice and a shaker and a record sheet for each player. The board and tiles are not needed. Each player throws both dice, adds the numbers thrown and colours in on his record sheet the total number of small squares the throw indicates. When one player has coloured in both floors, the game ends and everyone counts their squares to work out the finishing order. Ask the children what 'cm²' means. What does each cm² represent? How do we write square metres? Explaining the superscript ² is not easy. It may be best presented as meaning 'squared' and rely on a fuller interpretation when square numbers are introduced. If this causes problems, fall back on to the longhand 'square centimetres' or 'square metres'. Again, go over how many square 'metres' would be needed to finish each room. Can the children work out the length of the perimeter of each 'real' room from the plan? How is this done?

HOW TO PLAY THE LION AND THE ROSE

For 2 to 4 players

YOU NEED: the game board, a dice and shaker, and a set of 'lion' and a set of 'rose' floor tiles for each player.

❶ Sort out the playing order.

❷ Take turns to throw the dice and lay down from your sets the number of tiles shown.

❸ If 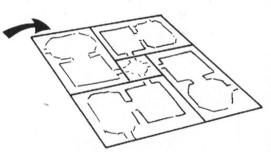 or are thrown, that throw does not count and play passes on to the next player.

❹ The first player to cover both floors is the winner.

CENTRE PIECE FOR GAME BOARD

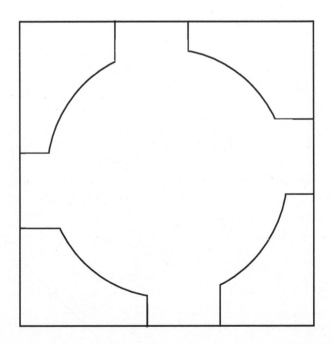

Arrange four room layouts at right angles to each other around the centre piece.

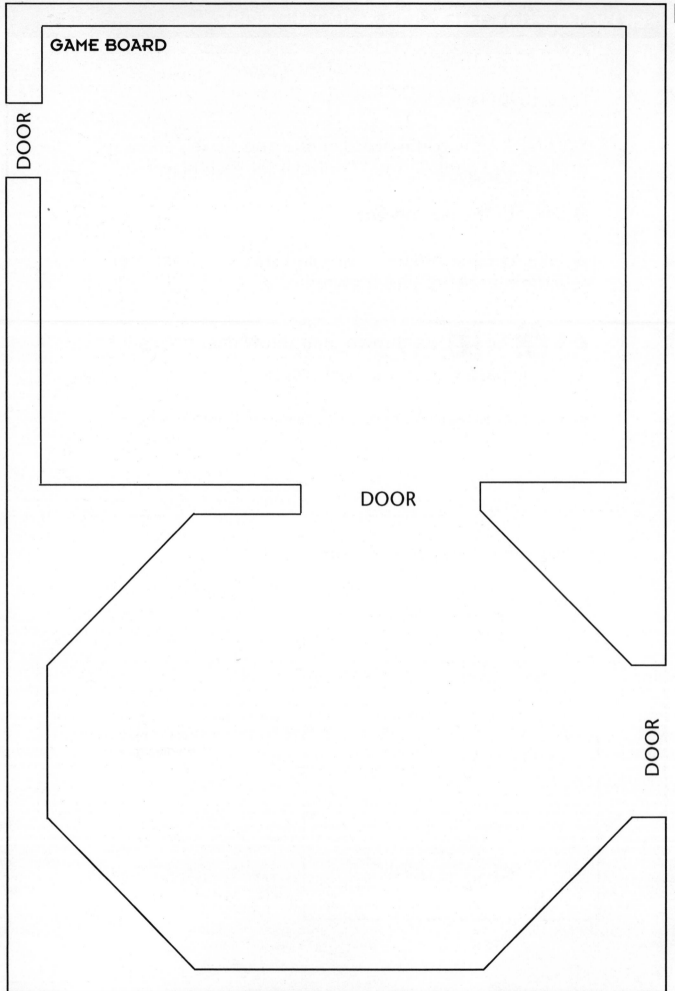

GAME BOARD

DOOR

DOOR

DOOR

x4

LION AND ROSE TILES

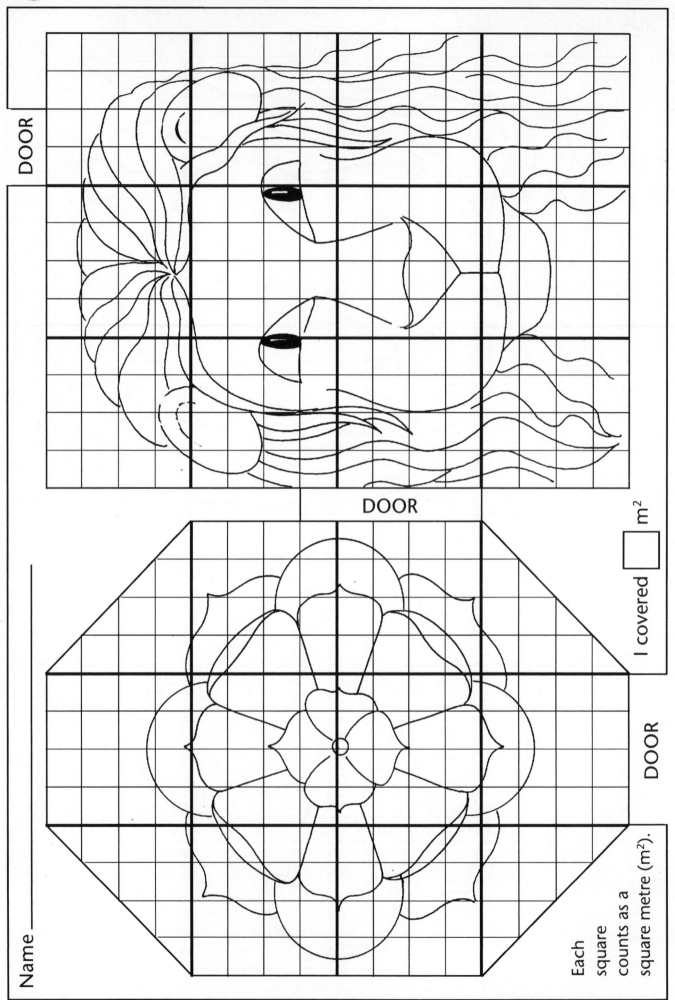

DOOR

DOOR

DOOR

Name

Each
square
counts as a
square metre (m²).

I covered ☐ m²

GUESS WHAT?

WHAT YOU NEED

PHOTOCOPIABLE PAGES
Game sheet 76, or a modified version.
FOR CONSTRUCTION
No special requirements.
FOR PLAYING
Various measuring instruments and items to be measured (see 'Preparation'), a game sheet and pencil for every player, calculators (optional).

TEACHING CONTENT

★ Practising measuring skills (SSM: 1e; ME: C/D)
★ Comparing estimation skills (SSM: 4a; ME: C/D)
★ Using measuring instruments to check estimates (SSM: 4b; ME: C/D)

PREPARATION

Assembling the game: Setting up this game requires some forethought and planning around the dimensions of the teaching space. However, the game allows extensive practice in estimation and, furthermore, gives a rough and ready guide to the children's competence in estimating. The children will need the following equipment or similar (in which case amend the game sheet): a litre measure and a container holding at least 4l, for example a bucket; a measuring jug with millilitre divisions and a container holding less than 1l; a scale with kilogram weights and an item weighing in excess of 3kg, for example a builder's brick; metre measuring sticks, preferably without subdivisions and an object or distance over 2m long, for example the width of the classroom; a centimetre tape and a short length, for example the circumference of a large plant pot; a stopwatch or clock timer and an 'event' such as the sinking of a holed plastic container in a bucket of water. The children's estimates and the exact measurements are filled in on the game sheet (photocopiable page 76).
Introducing the game: Explain how each child's ability to estimate and measure will be established. The difference between their estimates and the 'true' values determine the points. The better the estimate the less points they get and the more likely they are to win. Discuss how this sum is done – taking the smaller number from the larger.

HOW TO PLAY

Play this game over a long period with the equipment left out around the room. Every player must fill in all the estimates on the game sheet before carrying out the actual measuring. When *everyone* has completed the sheets, they can be checked against the average result or the teacher's own findings. The best estimator will have the least total difference between his estimates and his measurements and, thus, the least points.

TEACHER'S ROLE

It is likely that you will have to help the children with the filling in of their game sheets and with the practical tasks. This input can be lessened if you go carefully through the various estimation tasks beforehand. Once they have started, try to get the children to help each other.

GAME VARIATION

Play the game as before, except that the children acquire an accuracy percentage (AP) for each task and an overall Average Accuracy Percentage (AAP) at the end. For example: if the estimate is 2l and the measure is 5l, then AP = $2 \div 5 \times 100 = 40\%$. You may need to explain that the AAP is found by adding all the APs together and dividing by the number of them (6). The AAPs can be put in rank order to find the best estimator in the class. Amend the game sheet as shown opposite.

The _____		
Estimate		secs
Measure		secs
Accuracy percentage		%

GAME SHEET FOR GUESS WHAT?

Name _____

The _____

Estimate ⬜ l

Measure ⬜ l

Difference ⬜ points

The _____

Estimate ⬜ ml

Measure ⬜ ml

Difference ⬜ points

The _____

Estimate ⬜ kg

Measure ⬜ kg

Difference ⬜ points

The _____

Estimate ⬜ secs

Measure ⬜ secs

Difference ⬜ points

The _____

Estimate ⬜ m

Measure ⬜ m

Difference ⬜ points

The _____

Estimate ⬜ cm

Measure ⬜ cm

Difference ⬜ points

TOTAL POINTS

_____

REMOVALS

WHAT YOU NEED

PHOTOCOPIABLE PAGES
Van sheet 79, crates sheets 80 and 81, record sheet 82, 'How to play' sheet 78.

FOR CONSTRUCTION
Card, scissors, adhesive, paper clips, coloured pens or crayons, marker pen.

FOR PLAYING
Removal van and six crates numbered 1–6 per player, a dice and shaker, 'How to play' sheet, a record strip for each player.

Number the crates like this before assembling them.

TEACHING CONTENT

☆ Simulating a real-life situation to give experience of volumes (SSM: 1e; ME: D)

☆ Using cm³ and applying them as a scale unit of m³ (SSM: 4c; ME: D)

PREPARATION

Assembling the game: For this game each player needs a model removal van and a set of six crates. Nets are provided for the van and four of the six crates, so you will need two copies of photocopiable page 81 per player. Copy all the nets directly on to card. Write a number value or dice spots into each square on the sides of each crate. Before assembling them, each set of crates and one van can be coloured in the same colour – a red set, a yellow set and so on. Hold the vans and crates with paper clips while you construct them to allow the adhesive to dry thoroughly.

Introducing the game: Some of the children will have experience of moving house. Discuss how expertly removal firms load their vans. Let the children experiment with loading the model vans with the crates.

HOW TO PLAY

This is a game for two to four players. Everyone's crates are piled in the centre. Each player throws the dice and chooses a crate with the same number to put in her van. If a player does not want a particular crate, it can be rejected, but play passes on to the next player. If there is no crate left for a throw, that player cannot do anything and play passes on too. The vans can be filled in any way, but if too many crates of one size are used it may be difficult for that player to finish filling his van exactly. The first player to fill her van without any spaces wins. The finishing positions are based on the number of crates each player has 'loaded'.

TEACHER'S ROLE

Ask the players to measure the lengths of the sides of their crates. Do the children know what 'volume' means? Explain how the volume of each crate is calculated and that this is written as 'so many cm³'; the 'cubed' showing that three dimensions have been measured. Ask the children to work out the volume of each crate in their vans and add them up. Whose van is carrying the largest volume? Are the finishing positions fair? If they were based on volume filled/left to be filled would they be the same? (First will be the same, but the rest may not be.) The children should begin to see that the number of crates is not as important as their sizes. Pose the problem: If we had as many of each crate as we liked in what different ways could we load the vans? Make a list of different combinations of crates which fill the van exactly. Finally, ask the children what the volumes of the crates would be if each 1cm³ was 1m³?

GAME VARIATION

Colouring the sets of crates and vans simplifies the game. The game is played as before, except that the children have no choice in selecting the crates and just aim to collect the full set in their colour. After the game, give each player a record strip (photocopiable page 82) to complete.

HOW TO PLAY REMOVALS

For 2 to 4 players

YOU NEED: a van and a set of six crates for each player, a dice and shaker.

❶ Sort out the playing order.

❷ Throw the dice in turn and select a matching crate.

❸ Your van can be filled in any way.

❹ If there is no crate left for a number, the throw is wasted and play passes on to the next player.

❺ The first player to fill her or his van wins and the game ends.

❻ Work out the final positions: first, second, third or fourth.

REMOVAL VAN NET

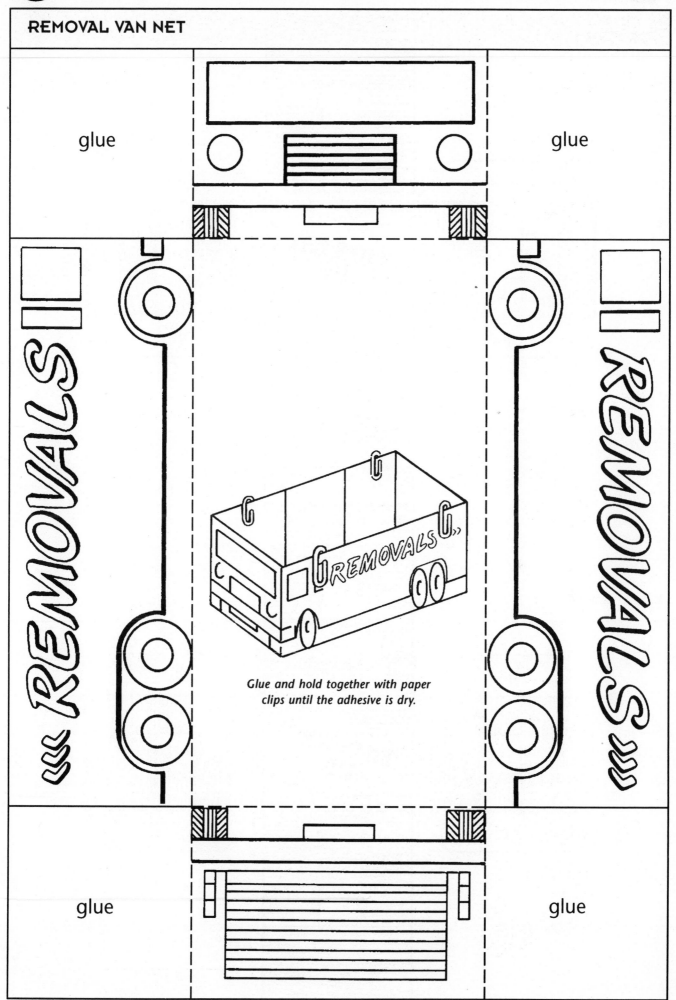

glue

glue

REMOVALS

REMOVALS

Glue and hold together with paper
clips until the adhesive is dry.

glue

glue

CRATES 1

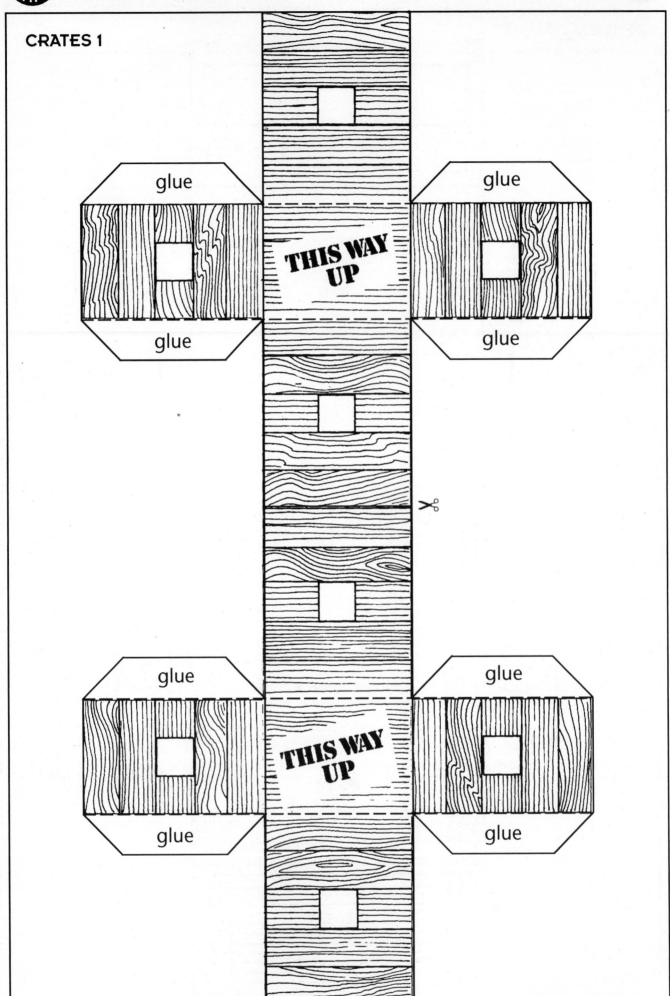

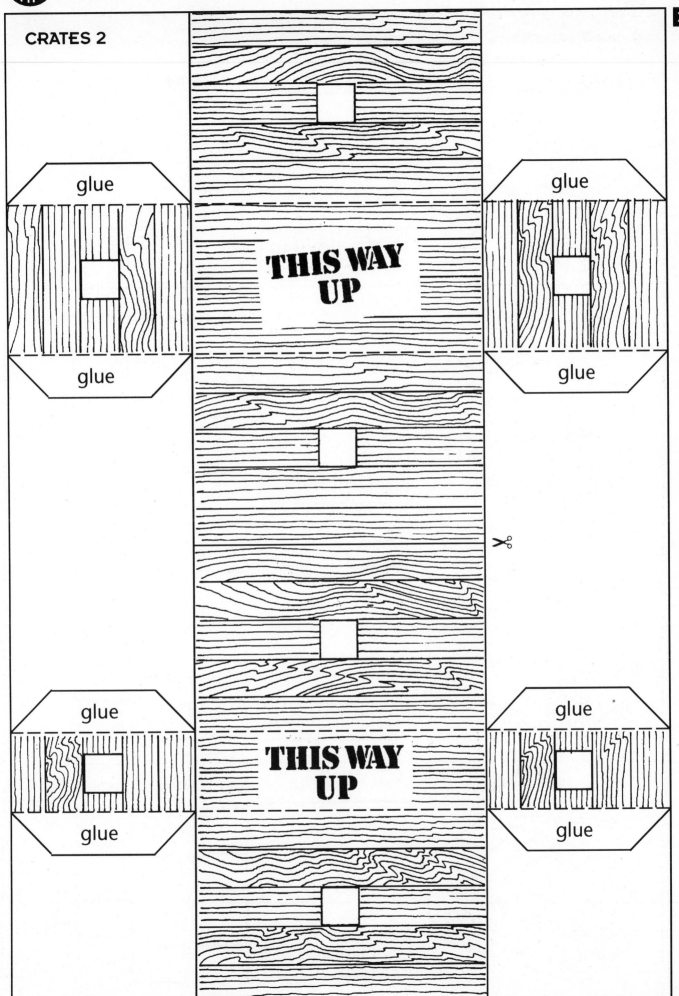

RECORD SHEET FOR REMOVALS

Name _____

| 1st | 2nd | 3rd | 4th |

My removal van carries

[ ] cm³ + [ ] cm³ +

[ ] cm³ + [ ] cm³ +

[ ] cm³ + [ ] cm³ =

[ ] cm³

Name _____

| 1st | 2nd | 3rd | 4th |

My removal van carries

[ ] cm³ + [ ] cm³ +

[ ] cm³ + [ ] cm³ +

[ ] cm³ + [ ] cm³ =

[ ] cm³

Name _____

| 1st | 2nd | 3rd | 4th |

My removal van carries

[ ] cm³ + [ ] cm³ +

[ ] cm³ + [ ] cm³ +

[ ] cm³ + [ ] cm³ =

[ ] cm³

Name _____

| 1st | 2nd | 3rd | 4th |

My removal van carries

[ ] cm³ + [ ] cm³ +

[ ] cm³ + [ ] cm³ +

[ ] cm³ + [ ] cm³ =

[ ] cm³

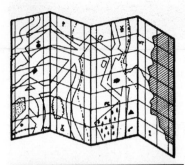

WHAT YOU NEED

PHOTOCOPIABLE PAGES
Letter/number grid sheet 138, OS map symbol cards sheets 139 and 140, map sheet 85, 'How to play' sheet 84.

FOR CONSTRUCTION
Card, scissors, adhesive, paper clips.

FOR PLAYING
Map of 'Anywhere', letter/ number grid, 3-D OS map symbol cards, an opaque bag of 1–10 number cards, A–F letter dice and shaker, a pencil and eraser or different-coloured pen for each player.

ANYWHERE

TEACHING CONTENT

☆ Using letter/number coordinates to identify squares on a grid (SSM: 3b; PM: B)
☆ Familiarising children with OS map symbols

PREPARATION

Assembling the game: For this game the letter/number grid given in the Special Section (photocopiable page 138) is used together with the stand-up 3-D OS map symbol cards (photocopiable pages 139 and 140). The grid does not necessarily have to be mounted on card as its main function is to hold the OS map symbol cards and provide each with an identifying code for playing the game. The map symbol cards should be copied on to card and then assembled as directed in the Special Section (see page 135). The map of 'Anywhere' (photocopiable page 85) is both part of the game and a record of it. The children will need one map per group. A paper photocopy will be sufficient. Provide the children with pencils and erasers, as mistakes will be frequent initially. Make a letter dice by sticking labels on the faces of a dice and writing on A to F. Also, the players will need an opaque bag containing a set of 1–10 number cards.

Introducing the game: The children should have had experience of maps, ideally those described in the Special Section (see page 135), and OS map symbols prior to playing this game. Ask the children to match the symbol cards to symbols on the map. For example, having found a church, elaborate on it: What type is it? Where is it?

HOW TO PLAY

The OS map symbol cards are placed on the grid by the players, one at a time and anywhere they like. In turn, each player throws the letter dice and chooses a number card from the bag of ten, giving the coordinates of a square. If there is a card on it, this is taken off and the matching symbol is ringed on the map. If there is nothing on the chosen square play passes on to the next player. This continues until 20 items on the map are ringed. The player ringing the twentieth symbol wins the game.

TEACHER'S ROLE

Throughout the game reinforce the children's knowledge of coordinates and OS map symbols. As a symbol card is taken off the grid, ask the children what the coordinates are of the squares around it? Ask the children if the symbol makes sense to them. Some of the symbols have a strong pictorial link – the windmill or coniferous wood – while others, such as the station or level crossing, need a little more thought. Check that the children are ringing items on the map correctly. They should not be afraid of drawing a large ring around a wood or a line of pylons.

GAME VARIATIONS

• Give each player a coloured pen. Then the winner could be the player who rings the most symbols out of a set number.
• For a really long game, go for full completion of the map. Again, give the children coloured pencils, so that the winner can be identified easily.

HOW TO PLAY ANYWHERE

For 2 or more players

YOU NEED: map of 'Anywhere', 3-D OS map symbol cards, the letter/number grid, an A–F letter dice and shaker, 1–10 number cards and an opaque bag, a pencil or different-coloured pen or pencil for each player.

❶ Put the 3-D OS map symbol cards on the grid anywhere you like.

❷ Sort out the playing order.

❸ Take turns to throw the dice to pick a column, and then choose a number card out of the bag to show the row. Together these give the coordinates of a square from which to take off the OS map card. Put a ring (in your colour) round the same OS symbol on the map.

❹ If there is no card on that square, those choices are wasted and play passes on to the next player.

❺ Keep doing this until 20 symbol cards are taken off the grid.

❻ The player ringing the twentieth symbol is the winner.

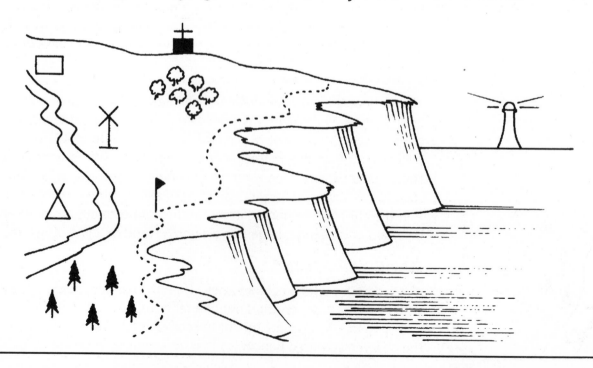

MAP OF 'ANYWHERE'

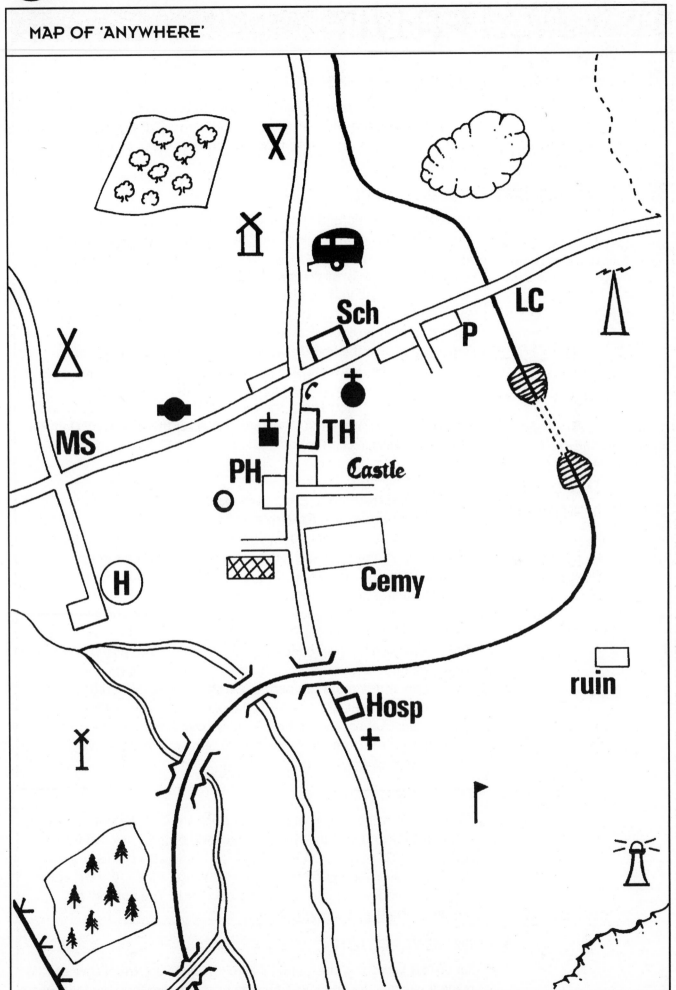

Sch

P

LC

MS

TH

Castle

PH

Cemy

H

ruin

Hosp

FRUIT

WHAT YOU NEED

PHOTOCOPIABLE PAGES
Game board sheet 88, 'How to play' sheet 87. For 360° version only: bearings compass sheet 144, degree randomiser sheet 142.

FOR CONSTRUCTION
Card, adhesive. For 360° version: paper fastener. For clockwise/anticlockwise version: correction fluid, marker pen.

FOR PLAYING
For 360° version: *modified game board, three counters for each player, 360° version of the degree randomiser, 'How to play' sheet.*
For clockwise/anticlockwise version: *modified game board, three counters for each player and one extra counter, a dice and shaker, 'How to play' sheet.*

TEACHING CONTENT

☆ Moving in clockwise and anticlockwise directions (SSM: 3c; PM: B)
☆ Familiarising the children with the 360° circle (SSM: 3c; A: D)
☆ Reading angles accurately, to within one degree of a 360° scale (SSM: 4b; A: D)

PREPARATION

There are two versions of this game, a clockwise/anticlockwise version and a 360° version, which require different preparations. For both versions each player needs three coins or counters.
Clockwise/anticlockwise version: Delete the 'Free choice' labels and print 'Change direction' in their places. Copy the new sheet and mount it on medium card. It can then be coloured in and laminated. An additional coin or counter is required as a playing piece.
360° version: Use the board as it is, but stick the bearings compass, minus its pointer, from the Special Section (photocopiable page 144) in the centre of the sheet in line with the arrow in the 'Free choice' segment at the top of the sheet. This is then mounted on to medium card and can be coloured and laminated. The 360° version of the degree randomiser from the Special Section (photocopiable page 142) is also required.

HOW TO PLAY

Clockwise/anticlockwise version: Each player chooses a fruit. To move, the players take turns to shake the dice and move a counter, the same one for everyone, in a clockwise direction round the board starting from the 'Change direction' segment. If the counter lands on the same fruit as that 'belonging' to the player making the move, she can put a coin on one of her fruit squares. If not, nothing happens. If the counter lands on 'Change direction' play goes in the opposite direction. The first player to cover all her three fruits wins – and collects everyone else's coins too!
360° version: Each player chooses a fruit. To move, the players take turns to make a three-digit number using the 360° version of the degree randomiser and find the segment in which that number occurs. If the fruit in that segment is the same as the player's, he can put a coin on one of his corner fruit squares. If it is not, play passes on to the next player. Every move is measured from 0°– the top arrow. The first player to cover all his three fruit wins.

TEACHER'S ROLE

Make sure that the players are moving clockwise/anticlockwise correctly and that they understand 'Change direction', or that they can find a certain number of degrees. To simplify the game, delete the single degrees to give just tens to count; in which case, stick a '0' card at the end of the randomiser and select only two cards. The number of segments could also be reduced.

GAME VARIATION

For quicker versions of the games, if a fruit is identified, irrespective of who made the move, the player with that fruit can put a coin on her fruit square.

HOW TO PLAY FRUIT

360° VERSION
For 2 to 4 players

YOU NEED: the game board, three counters for each player, 360° version of the degree randomiser with cards and bag.

❶ Each choose a different fruit.

❷ Take turns to make a three-digit degree number with the randomiser.

❸ Go to that number of degrees.

❹ If it is in a segment with one of your fruit, you can put a counter on one of the fruit in your corner.

❺ If you land on one of someone else's fruit, play passes on to the next player.

❻ The first player to cover all his or her three fruit is the winner.

CLOCKWISE/ANTICLOCKWISE VERSION
For 2 to 4 players

YOU NEED: the game board, three counters for each player plus one more counter, a dice and shaker.

❶ Each choose a different fruit. Put the extra counter on the top 'Change direction' segment.

❷ Take turns to throw the dice. Move the counter that number of fruit segments clockwise round the board.

❸ If you land on 'Change direction' go the other way round the board.

❹ If you land on one of your fruit, you can put a counter on one of the fruit in your corner.

❺ If you land on one of someone else's fruit, play passes on to the next player.

❻ The first player to cover all her or his three fruit is the winner.

FRUIT GAME BOARD

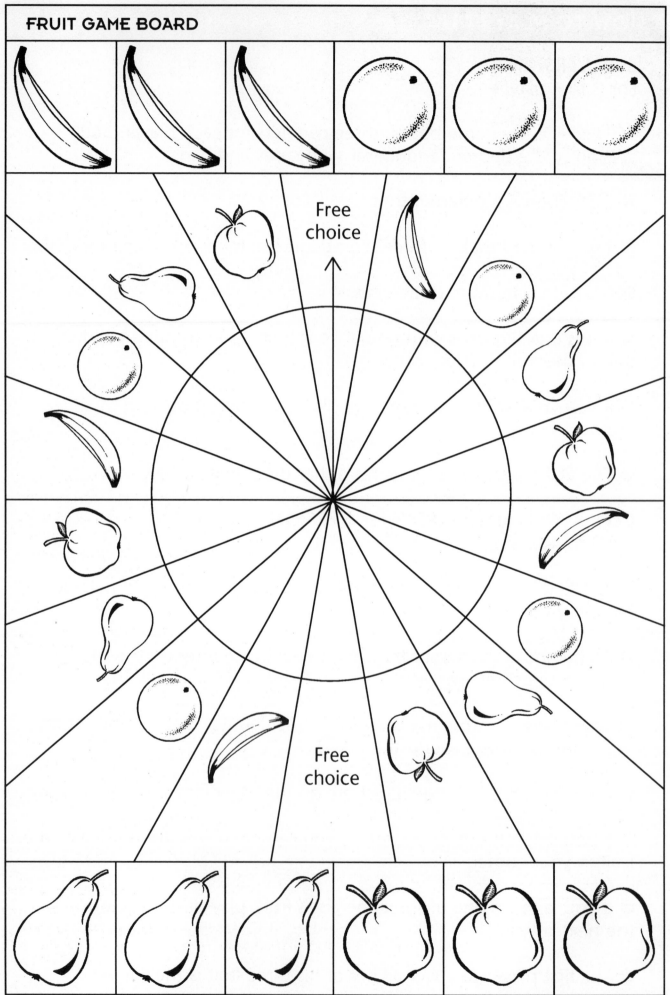

Free choice

Free choice

UFO

TEACHING CONTENT

★ Using angles between 0° and 90° in a game situation (N: 1a; A: D)
★ Measuring accurately degrees between 0° and 90° (SSM: 3c; A: D)
★ Using a 90° quadrant to one degree of accuracy (SSM: 4b; A: D)

PREPARATION

This game uses the degree randomiser and 90° quadrant given in the Special Section (pages 142 and 144) together with a game board sheet (photocopiable page 91). Photocopy the UFO game board sheet and copy the 90° quadrant from the Special Section. Cut out the quadrant and stick it in the bottom-right hand corner of the UFO sheet. Mount the UFO sheet on to medium-thick card. Paste or copy the pointer for the quadrant on to card, cut off the 'sighting' section and fasten the pointer on to the quadrant on the UFO sheet with a paper fastener. Hold the paper fastener in place, and protect the children's fingers, by putting sticky tape over the fastener, on the back of the sheet. The players will also need paper and pencils for scoring.

HOW TO PLAY

In this game for two or more players, each player in turn makes a number using the 90° version of the degree randomiser and moves the pointer to that angle. If it lines up on a UFO, that spaceship is hit and the player gets the points on that particular UFO. If more than one UFO is on the line of the pointer, then they all count as hit. The UFO's can be hit more than once. If the pointer doesn't touch anything, play passes on to the next player. The first player to get 50 points or more wins.

WHAT YOU NEED

PHOTOCOPIABLE PAGES
UFO game board sheet 91, 90° quadrant sheet 144, degree randomiser sheet 142, 'How to play' sheet 90.

FOR CONSTRUCTION
Medium-thick card, adhesive, paper fastener, sticky tape, scissors.

FOR PLAYING
UFO game board with 90° quadrant, 90° version of the degree randomiser, paper and pencil for each player.

TEACHER'S ROLE

During the game, check that the players understand the scale on the quadrant, in particular the five degree half-way lines.

GAME VARIATIONS

• Instead of the emphasis being on addition, each player could be given a set number of 'ammunition' points and each UFO hit is deducted from that number.
• Draw in more UFOs with more number values including tens or hundreds.
• When adding UFOs allow for the quadrant in the corner. The original UFO sheet could be photocopied and used as a record sheet with children colouring in their hits in their own colours. In which case, once a UFO has been hit, it crash lands and is out of the game.

HOW TO PLAY UFO

For 2 or more players

YOU NEED: UFO game board, 90° version of the degree randomiser with digital cards in an opaque bag.

❶ Sort out the playing order.

❷ In turn make a degree number between 0° and 90° using the degree randomiser.

❸ Move the pointer on to that exact angle.

❹ If the pointer touches a UFO, that spaceship is hit and you get the points on it.

❺ If the pointer touches more than one UFO, they all count as hit.

❻ If the pointer does not touch a UFO, play goes on to the next player.

❼ The first player to get 50 points or more wins.

GAME BOARD FOR UFO

ROUGHLY RIGHT

TEACHING CONTENT

☆ Extending the children's practical knowledge of measuring systems (SSM: 1b; ME: C)
☆ Knowing rough metric and Imperial equivalents still in daily use (SSM: 4a; ME: D)

PREPARATION

Assembling the game: This is a pair matching game for metric and Imperial equivalents. Copy the cards directly on to card or mount them and then cut them out. The conversion guide does not have a direct role in the game, but is there for reference. You might like to provide each player with an A3 photocopy of the guide as a playmat (or an A5 copy as a handy reminder card to help with other maths work).

Introducing the game: Do not put too much stress on metric and Imperial equivalents. While it is useful for the children to know them, there is little sense in learning them off by heart. This game is meant to make the children aware of the similarities, but not drown them in detail. Before the game, go through the conversion guide with the children. Draw out examples from their experience such as milk in pint bottles.

HOW TO PLAY

The players have to understand that they are trying to match a metric measurement with an Imperial measurement forming a pair. Shuffle the cards and spread them out face down on the table. In turn, the players turn over any two cards. If they match, they can keep the pair. If they do not match, they are put back face down. The skill is to try to remember which card is where. Play continues in this way until the last pair are taken. The player who has the most pairs is the winner.

TEACHER'S ROLE

Most of the cards are straight forward equivalents. Expect questions about those cards without units, such as the speed restriction signs, where common sense must be applied. Similarly, the children should know that 1000g = 1kg and so be able to work out the equivalent for the bag of sweets (the jar of jam). Remind the children that they are matching *quantities*, so they may not be matching like for like: compost, a solid, is measured by volume and matches the paint which is measured by capacity too. Discuss similarities and anomalies like these. Explain how the Imperial system was full of different number bases which meant people didn't have to handle large numbers, as we have to do in the metric system: 16 oz = 1lb, 14 lb = 1st, 8st = 1cwt (a hundredweight) and 20cwt = 1t (a ton). The largest number anyone had to count to was 20. So there were advantages for people who never went to school and never learned to count in hundreds, let alone thousands. Collect labels and other examples of metric and Imperial measurements for a classroom display. Tables of the 'old-fashioned' Imperial measurements give the children chance to use their calculators to work out all sorts of measuring equivalents: How many inches tall are you? How many ounces do you weigh? How many pints does that bucket hold?

HOW TO PLAY ROUGHLY RIGHT

For 2 or more players

YOU NEED: the conversion guide, the conversion cards.

❶ Shuffle the cards and spread them out face down.

❷ Sort out the playing order, then take turns.

❸ Turn over any two cards and place them face up on the table. If they make a pair you can keep them. If they do not match, turn them face down again.

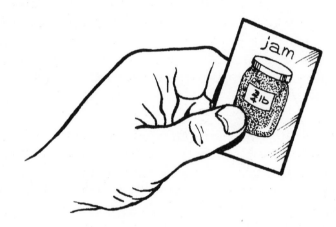

❹ The trick is to try to remember which cards are where to help you to turn over matching cards to make a pair. Use the conversion guide to remind you which cards go together.

❺ The player with the most pairs when all the cards have been matched up is the winner.

CONVERSION GUIDE

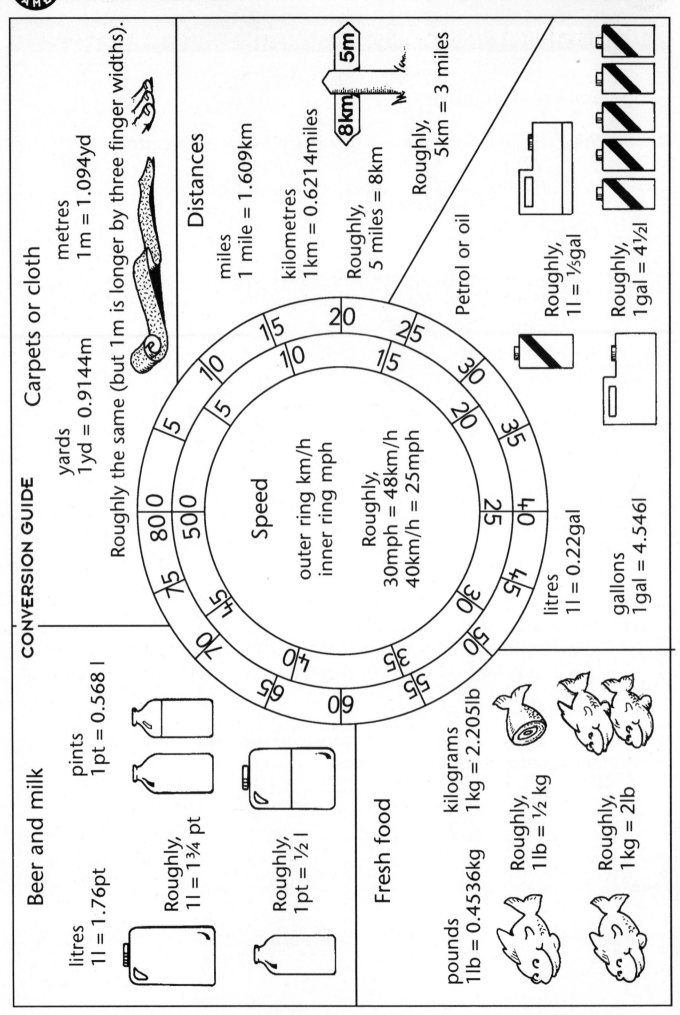

Carpets or cloth

metres
1m = 1.094yd

yards
1yd = 0.9144m

Roughly the same (but 1m is longer by three finger widths).

Distances

miles
1 mile = 1.609km

kilometres
1km = 0.6214miles

Roughly,
5 miles = 8km

5m

8km

Roughly,
5km = 3 miles

Petrol or oil

Roughly,
1l = ⅕gal

Roughly,
1gal = 4½l

litres
1l = 0.22gal

gallons
1gal = 4.546l

Speed

outer ring km/h
inner ring mph

Roughly,
30mph = 48km/h
40km/h = 25mph

Beer and milk

litres
1l = 1.76pt

pints
1pt = 0.568 l

Roughly,
1l = 1¾ pt

Roughly,
1pt = ½ l

Fresh food

kilograms
1kg = 2.205lb

pounds
1lb = 0.4536kg

Roughly,
1lb = ½ kg

Roughly,
1kg = 2lb

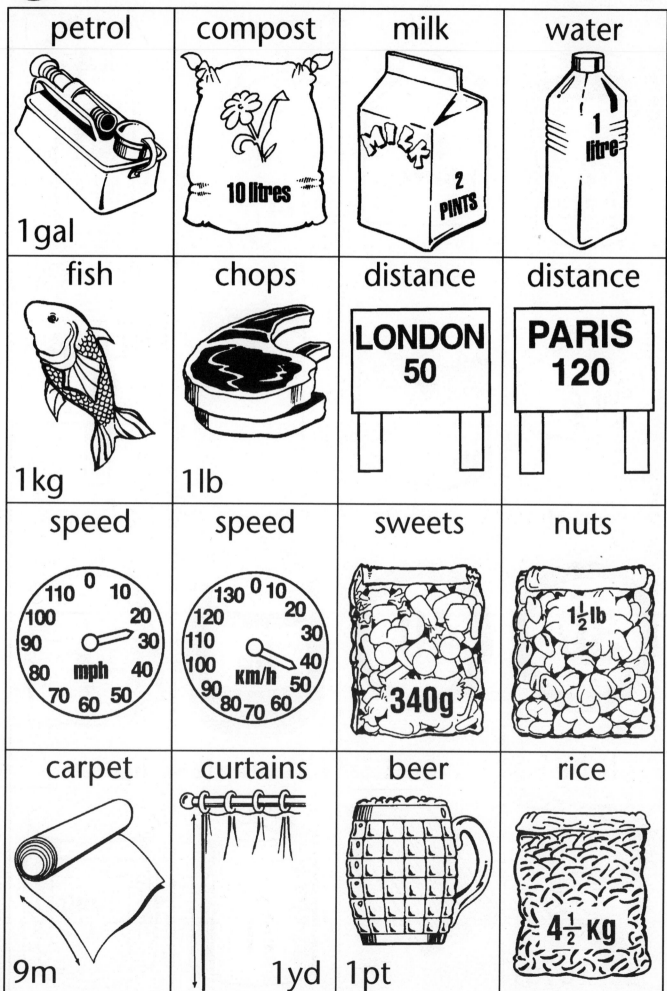

petrol

1 gal

compost

10 litres

milk

2 PINTS

water

1 litre

fish

1 kg

chops

1 lb

distance

LONDON 50

distance

PARIS 120

speed

mph

speed

km/h

sweets

340g

nuts

1½ lb

carpet

9m

curtains

1 yd

beer

1 pt

rice

4½ kg

paint	oil	milk	water
2 gals	4½ litres	2l	3½ pts

butter	sugar	distance	distance
500g	2lb	EDINBURGH 75	ROMA 80

speed	speed	jam	potatoes
30	40	¾ lb	

rope	wood	lemonade	apricots
10yds	1m	½ l	750g

WEB

TEACHING CONTENT

☆ Measuring angles accurately to within one degree on the 360° scale (SSM: 4b; A: D)
☆ Measuring bearings and distances accurately (SSM: 1e; PM: E)

WHAT YOU NEED

PHOTOCOPIABLE PAGES
Web segment sheet 99, record sheet 100, degree randomiser and digital cards sheet 142, bearings compass and pointer sheet 144, 'How to play' sheet 98.
FOR CONSTRUCTION
Card, adhesive, scissors, paper fastener, sticky tape.
FOR PLAYING
Web game board, 360° version of the degree randomiser and digital cards in an opaque bag, a different-coloured pen or crayon for each player, a group record sheet.

PREPARATION

During this game the children practise measuring angles and distances. To do this, the bearings compass (Special Section page 144) is used as an integral part of the game board. Make four copies of the web segment (photocopiable page 99) and mount them on to medium-thick cardboard. When they are dry, cut out the web as a circular game board. Photocopy and cut out the bearings compass and mount it in the exact centre of the web. Finally, mount the pointer on card and fasten it in the middle of the web with a paper fastener. Stick tape over the back of the fastener to hold it in place and to protect the children's fingers. Also needed are the 360° version of the degree randomiser (Special Section page 142) and the group record sheet (photocopiable page 100).

HOW TO PLAY

Give each player a different-coloured pen. In turn, each player makes a three-digit degree number with the randomiser and moves the pointer to that angle. The player decides how far along the pointer to go by replacing the digital cards in the bag and then deciding whether to choose two or three more cards before drawing them out. These cards must be arranged to make a number to fit the scale on the pointer; that is, one between 40mm and 160mm inclusive. If a number cannot be made to fit, play passes on to the next player. When an angle and a distance have been worked out to identify a space, the player colours in the identical space on the record sheet in her colour. When 20 spaces have been coloured, the game stops and the players count their scores. The winner is the player with the highest score.

TEACHER'S ROLE

Playing this game is an excellent assessment of how well the children can read the 360° compass and how well they have assimilated the concept of finding a particular place by measuring along the pointer. Pose the question: What if the board was bigger, what could we use as a pointer? (A ruler.) Where would we put a ruler for it to work in just the same way? (Put the 0mm point at the centre and line up the ruler on the angle.) What if every millimetre on the scale counted for 1m, what would the distances be in our game? What if they stood for kilometres?

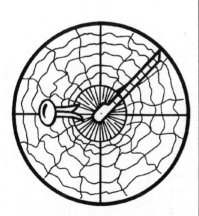

Assemble four copies of the web segment at right angles to each other.
Fix the bearings compass and pointer in the centre.

GAME VARIATIONS

• Delete the numbers on the web segment and the record sheet and have the winner as the player with the most coloured in spaces.
• Instead of colouring in the record sheet, the players could tally their scores. The first player to reach a predetermined score wins. In this case, the same space can be counted more than once as its 'ownership' is not limited by it being coloured.

HOW TO PLAY WEB

For 2 to 4 players

YOU NEED: the game board, a record sheet, a different-coloured pen for each player, the 360° version of the degree randomiser with its bag of digital cards.

❶ Choose a coloured pen each.

❷ In turn, make a three-digit degree number as shown on the degree randomiser.

❸ Move the pointer on the game board to that number of degrees.

❹ Now work out how far along the pointer to go. Do this by taking out two or three digital cards from the bag (you have the choice of how many). Arrange the cards to make a number between 40mm and 160mm. If you have chosen three cards and cannot make a low enough number, play passes on to the next player. If the number is alright, move along the pointer that number of millimetres to a space.

❺ Colour the same space on the record sheet in your colour. If it is coloured already play passes on to the next player.

❻ When 20 spaces are coloured, stop and count your scores.

❼ Highest score wins.

WEB SEGMENT

x4

RECORD SHEET FOR WEB

Colour in the spaces you land on.

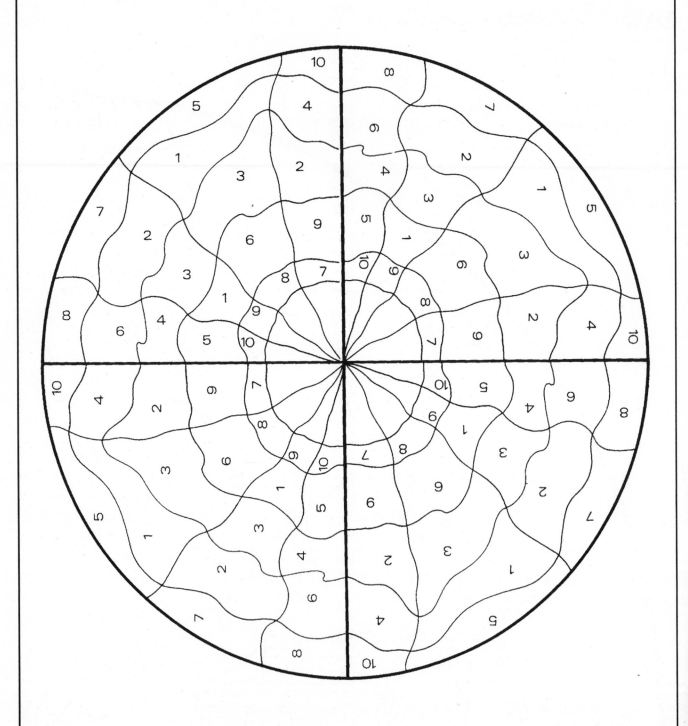

ROTO SYM

TEACHING CONTENT

★ Using different lines of symmetry (SSM: 2c; S: E)
★ Recognise reflective symmetry in a pattern (SSM: 3a; S: D/E)
★ Recognise rotational symmetry in a pattern (SSM: 3a; S: E)

PREPARATION

Photocopiable pages 103 and 104 give four different patterns demonstrating rotational symmetry. Each player will need a different pattern to collect. To help this game along, ideally there should be three sets of cards of the same pattern for each player (12 cards). Copy the patterns on to card and cut them up into individual cards; four per pattern. The cards are best uncoloured so that the designs are seen easily.

HOW TO PLAY

Put all the cards together as one pack and shuffle them. Deal out four to each player. The rest are placed in a stack face down in the middle. Everyone is trying to get four cards with identical patterns. This is done by taking the top card and exchanging it for one already in the hand. Exchanges or top cards that are not wanted are put on a discard stack face up alongside the pack. Instead of choosing the top card of the face down pack, a player can choose the top card of the discard stack. When a player has four cards the same, he puts the cards down in a square pattern to win.

TEACHER'S ROLE

After the game, explain some of the intricacies of the patterns. Put a mirror along some of the lines of reflection so that the children can see that the same pattern is repeated over and over again. Then ask the children to move each card through a right angle of rotation. What pattern is there now? Move through two, three and four right angles – is the pattern changed by rotation? What elements are needed for the patterns to be symmetrical when rotated or reflected? What shapes could we use besides circles in the patterns? Test out some shapes by rotating or reflecting them. Where could they be put on the 'petal' design cards, so that the cards are still symmetrical?

WHAT YOU NEED

PHOTOCOPIABLE PAGES
Roto sym cards sheets 103 and 104, 'How to play' sheet 102.
FOR CONSTRUCTION
Card, scissors.
FOR PLAYING
Three sets of cards of the same pattern for each player (12 cards each).

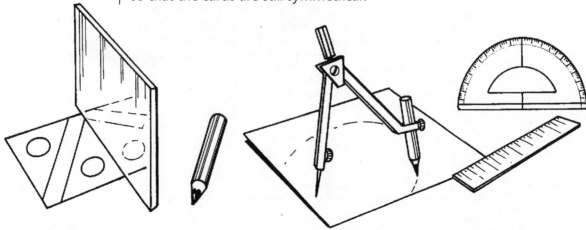

Using compasses and protractors, the children might like to make their own 'roto sym' patterns.

HOW TO PLAY ROTO SYM

For 2 to 4 players

YOU NEED: the 'Roto sym' cards.

❶ Shuffle the cards and then deal them out, one by one, four to each player.

❷ Place the rest of the pack face down in the middle.

❸ In turn, take the top card and exchange it for one of the four cards in your hand. Put this card on a face-up stack in the middle. You are aiming to collect four cards all the same.

❹ If the top card is not what you wanted, put it on the face-up stack.

❺ Instead of the top card on the face-down pack, you can choose to take the top card from the face-up stack.

❻ The first player to put down four identical cards in a square pattern wins.

x3

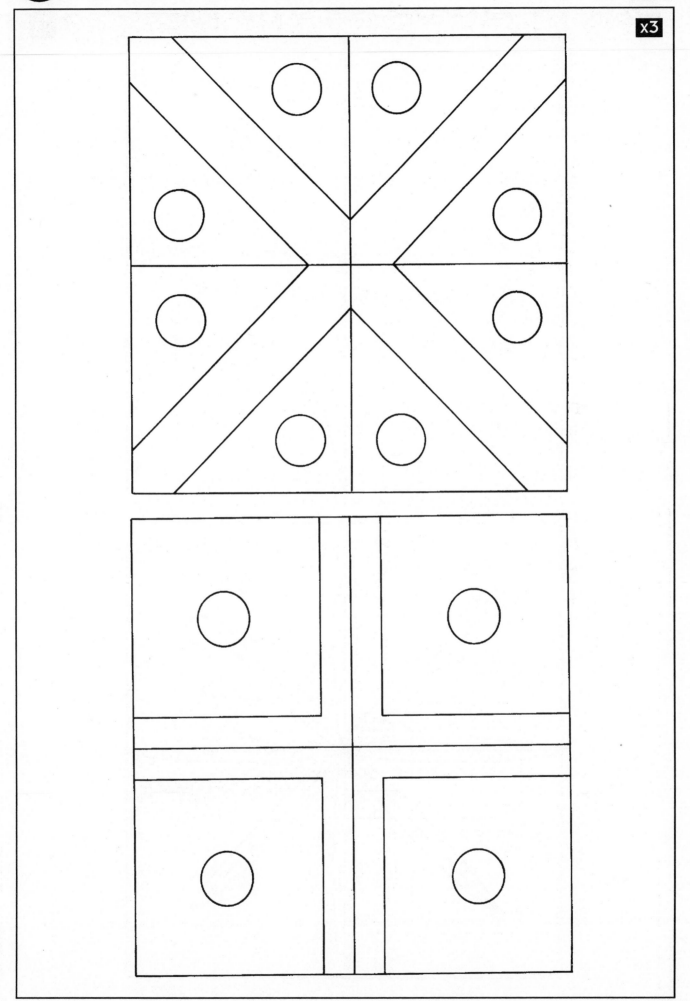

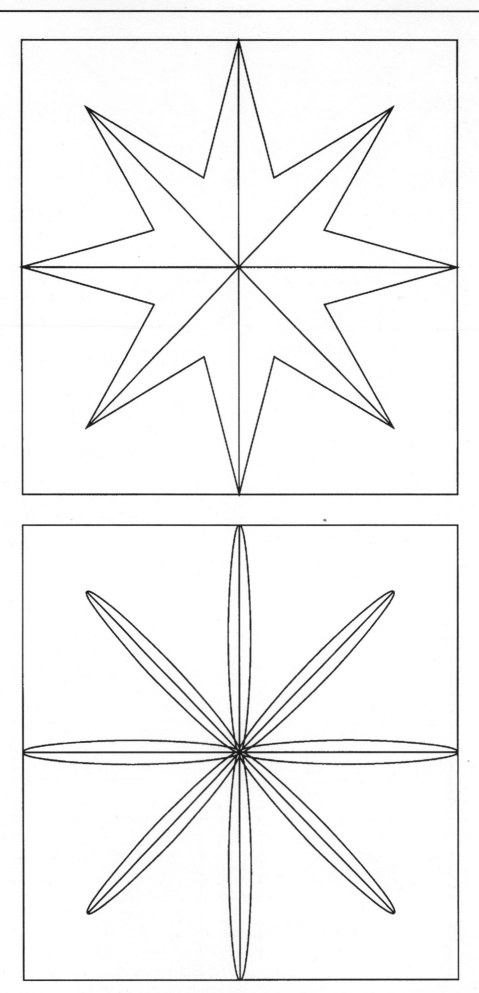

GAMES

WHEELS

WHAT YOU NEED

PHOTOCOPIABLE PAGES

Record strips sheet 107, 'How to play' sheet 106, degree randomiser and digital cards sheet 142.

FOR CONSTRUCTION

Cards, scissors (for degree randomiser).

FOR PLAYING

Record strip and pencil for each player, 360° version of the degree randomiser with opaque bag for digital cards, calculators.

+3rd number
119° = 412°

0°

52° 'wrap-over' from 3rd number

293°

1st number 080°

+2nd number
213° = 293°

TEACHING CONTENT

☆ Practising adding angles and dividing by 360° using a calculator (SSM: 3c; A: D)

☆ Making angles using three digits (SSM: 3c; A: D)

PREPARATION

Assembling the game: This paper, pencil and calculator game reinforces the 360° in a full circle. The players will need the 360° version of the degree randomiser from the Special Section (photocopiable page 142), and a record strip each (photocopiable page 107).

Introducing the game: In order to play this game, the players must have had experience of using a 360° protractor or the bearings compass in the Special Section (page 144). The players are not expected to measure degrees, although, hopefully, they will begin to anticipate when they have enough degrees for a 'wheel' or full circle.

HOW TO PLAY

In turn, each player makes up a number using the 360° version of the degree randomiser and writes it on his record strip. Play then passes on to the next player. The players keep making numbers, adding them to their previous total and dividing by 360 using a calculator. They can either colour in wheels as soon as they are 'acquired' (the total number of degrees is greater than 360) or they can keep adding and dividing each go until the total number of degrees, divided by 360, equals 4 point something and the player has enough degrees for four wheels. If they are collecting the wheels one at a time, any degrees over 360 can be carried on for the next wheel. Play continues to find second, third and fourth.

TEACHER'S ROLE

Play an introductory game – 'Spare wheel'. Give the children 360° protractors. Tell them to draw round them in a circle and mark 0°. Each child makes a number using the degree randomiser limited to 90° (see Special Section pages 136 and 142) and plots this angle from 0° on the circle. The children should then make a second number and plot it from the previous mark on the circumference by moving the protractor round to put the first mark on 0° or by adding the second number to the first and marking the total. Continue until each child has completed a spare wheel. There may be a remainder beyond 360°. In the full 'Wheels' game this wrap-over goes on to the next wheel. Throughout the 'Wheels' game, draw the players' attention to how many degrees are required to complete the wheel being 'acquired'. Ask questions to find out if the children are approximating numbers in their heads. They are unlikely to have exactly 360° for each wheel. How well do they understand the 'wrap-over' of the remainder? Go back to the 'Spare wheel' game if necessary.

GAME VARIATIONS

If three-digit numbers are too complex, or you want to concentrate on just making a 'spare wheel', then play a two-digit variant using the 90° version of the degree randomiser (see Special Section page 136).

HOW TO PLAY WHEELS

For 2 to 4 players

YOU NEED: a record strip and pencil for each player, a calculator, the 360° version of the degree randomiser with the digital cards in an opaque bag.

❶ Sort out the playing order.

❷ Take turns to make a three-digit degree number as shown on the degree randomiser.

❸ Write the number on your record sheet, then play passes on to the next player.

❹ Keep making numbers, adding them together and dividing by 360. When you have a complete circle, you can colour a wheel on your car.

❺ The first player to put four wheels on his or her car wins.

RECORD SHEET FOR WHEELS

Number of degrees ÷ 360 = Number of wheels

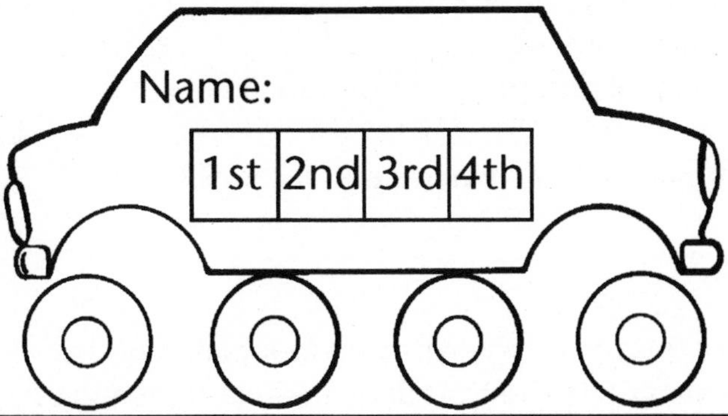

Name:

| 1st | 2nd | 3rd | 4th |

Number of degrees ÷ 360 = Number of wheels

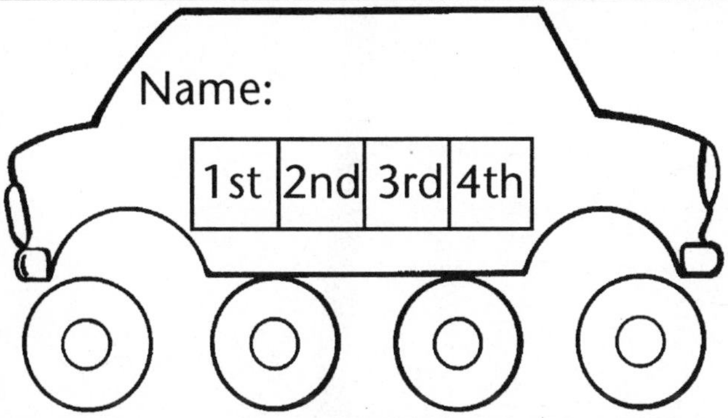

Name:

| 1st | 2nd | 3rd | 4th |

Number of degrees ÷ 360 = Number of wheels

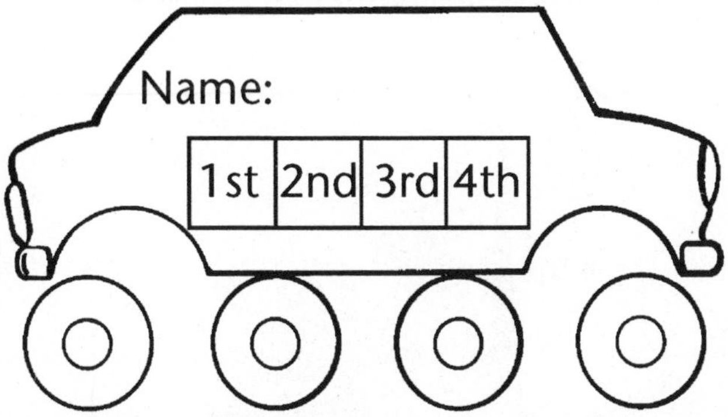

Name:

| 1st | 2nd | 3rd | 4th |

Number of degrees ÷ 360 = Number of wheels

Name:

| 1st | 2nd | 3rd | 4th |

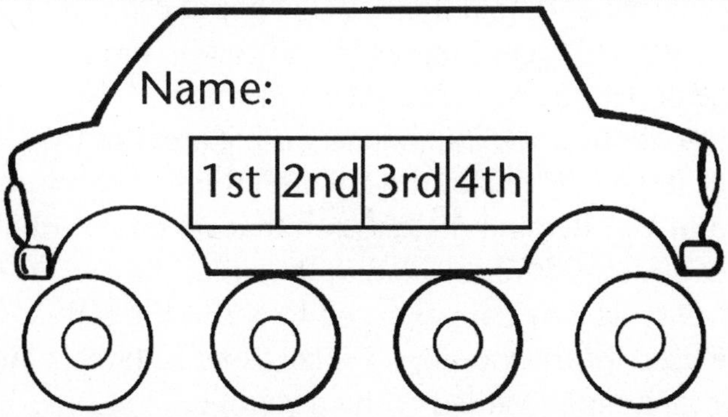

EXPEDITION

TEACHING CONTENT

☆ Simulating journey times (SSM: 4a; T: D)
☆ Converting hours to days (SSM: 4a; T: C)
☆ Exploring the relationship of distance in km and speed in km/h
(SSM: 4a; T: D)
☆ Converting decimal hours to days, minutes and seconds
(SSM: 4a; T: D)

PREPARATION

Assembling the game: For this game, you will need four copies of the 'map' given on photocopiable page 111. Arrange them at right angles around the centre piece. Make sure the half spaces on the centre piece match up with those on the map game board sections.

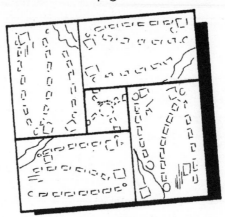

Assembling the game board

Mount the whole board on to thick card. You may wish to colour and then laminate it. Colour, cut out and assemble the playing pieces.

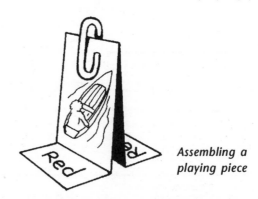

Assembling a playing piece

Either staple them together near the base (this will also add stability) or stick the two halves together and hold them with a paper clip until the adhesive is dry. You will need a full set of pieces in one colour and a record sheet for each player. This game uses a dice and shaker.
Introducing the game: Talk about travelling in inaccessible areas of the world and across difficult terrain. When do the children think they might travel by mule or need a guide? Remind the children that 24 hours equal one day and stress the two methods of calculating time that they will use while playing the game. Discuss why days are used to count the time for stopovers, but hours are used for the journeys. Explain how stopovers are needed to rest and to organise the next leg of the expedition.

WHAT YOU NEED

PHOTOCOPIABLE PAGES
Map layout sheet 111, centre and playing pieces sheet 112, 'How to play' sheet 110, record sheet 113, record sheet 114 (for game variation only).

FOR CONSTRUCTION
Thick card, scissors, adhesive, coloured pens or crayons.

FOR PLAYING
Game board, a set of five playing pieces for each player, a dice and shaker, a record sheet for each player, calculators.

HOW TO PLAY

Each player arranges his five playing pieces on one of the layouts making up the board, each piece next to its picture. All the players start on their Capital City and have to throw a six to start the plane journey. *Every* throw while on the Capital City circle is tallied on the record sheet and counts as a one day stopover. Once a six is thrown, the player can start on his journey. He can move the plane playing piece only one box at a time and then only if the right type of number is thrown: to move on to an E box, an even number must be thrown; to move on to an O box, an odd number must be thrown. *Every* throw on a journey counts as one hour of journey time and is tallied on the record sheet. Once the plane reaches Oasis Town, another six is needed to leave, this time by Land Rover. Again every throw used in getting a six represents a one day stopover. Continue like this to the last E box. Here another six is needed to reach the mountain summit. These throws also count as one hour of journey time. The first player to reach the summit wins, but play continues until everyone has finished. Then complete the record sheets – how long did all the journeys take?

TEACHER'S ROLE

After the game, go over the record sheets with the children. How long did each leg of journey take? Who stayed the longest in Riverville?

GAME VARIATION

This pencil, paper and calculator game variation employs the 4 × 4 game board as a reference point, rather like using a map. The game brings together distance and time to calculate 'speed', as well as practising conversions of units of time. Unlike the original game, every player progresses through the game itself at the same rate. Who actually completes the expedition in the shortest time is only revealed when players have finished all their calculations. Besides the 4 × 4 game board and a dice and shaker, each player needs a calculator and copy of the second record sheet (photocopiable page 114).

In the first round of dice throws, the dice number is filled in on the record sheet as the number of days spent at Capital City. In the second round, the number thrown is entered in the kilometre box for the distance, which is then divided by the speed given for the plane. (Please remember you are not 'stuck' with these speeds. They can be replaced with 'harder' numbers to emphasise 'long division'.) Rounds of dice

throws are carried on in this manner until all the boxes on the record sheet are filled with randomly thrown numbers.

You will probably need to help the players with their final calculations to find out whose expedition took the longest. Work out the total in days. The total number of hours of journey time needs to be divided by 24 to find the number of days to add on to the stopover days. If so desired, the remaining hours can be expressed as hours and minutes by multiplying the hour decimals by 60. The minutes and their decimals can be rounded up or down. If the children are really enthusiastic, instead of rounding off, convert the minutes decimals to seconds, again by multiplying by 60 and round up or down the last second. As can be appreciated, these quite sophisticated conversions of time units are put within the reach of children simply because of the use of the electronic calculator.

HOW TO PLAY EXPEDITION

For 2 to 4 players

YOU NEED: the game board, a dice and shaker, calculators, five playing pieces each, 'Expedition travel log' record sheet for each player.

❶ Each player arranges his or her five playing pieces in one section of the board by the correct pictures.

❷ All the players start on a Capital City. To get off any circle and begin a journey a ⚅ has to be thrown. While on a circle, tally *every* throw on your record sheet.
Each throw counts as one day in that place.

❸ Once on a journey, you can only move ONE box at a time and only if the right type of number is thrown:

- to move on to an E box, an even number must be thrown;

- to move on to an O box, an odd number must be thrown.

❹ Tally *every* throw made on your journey. Each throw counts as one hour, including the last throws to reach the mountain summit.

❺ The player who reaches the summit first wins, but play continues until everyone finishes. Now complete your 'Expedition travel logs'.

MAP

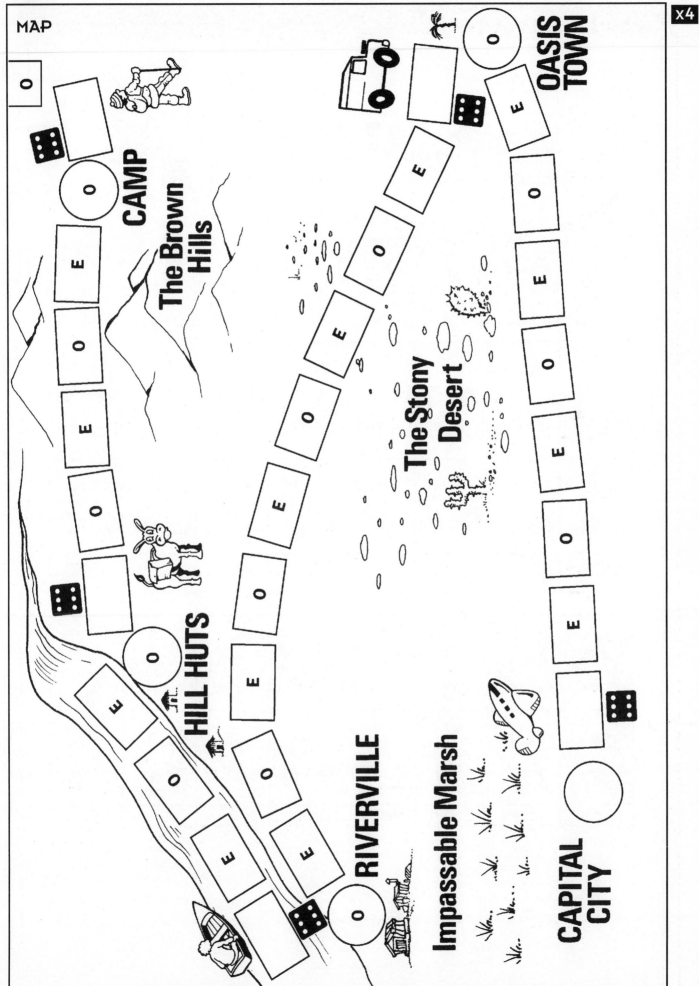

CAMP

The Brown Hills

OASIS TOWN

The Stony Desert

HILL HUTS

RIVERVILLE

Impassable Marsh

CAPITAL CITY

X4

CENTRE AND PLAYING PIECES

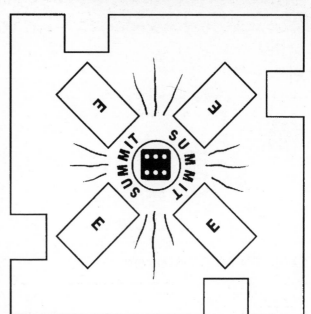

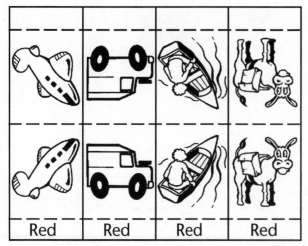

Red	Red	Red	Red

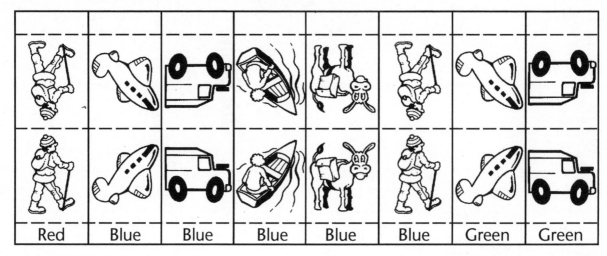

Red	Blue	Blue	Blue	Blue	Blue	Green	Green

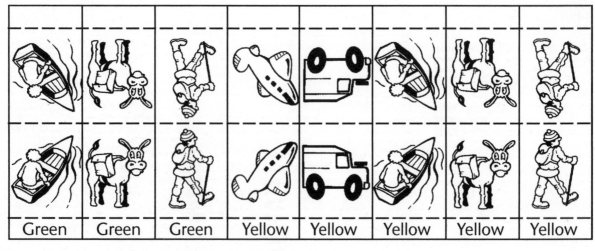

Green	Green	Green	Yellow	Yellow	Yellow	Yellow	Yellow

RECORD SHEET FOR EXPEDITION

Explorer's name:

Tally of throws
✓ (tick for each throw)

Colour

_____

	Tally of throws	
CAPITAL CITY stopover		☐ days
 ✈ PLANE journey		☐ hours
OASIS TOWN stopover		☐ days
 🚙 LAND ROVER journey		☐ hours
RIVERVILLE stopover		☐ days
 🛶 BOAT journey		☐ hours
HILL HUTS stopover		☐ days
 🐴 MULE journey		☐ hours
CAMP stopover		☐ days
 🚶 GUIDED journey		☐ hours

My expedition took ⬠ days (for stopovers) + ◯ hours (for journeys).

◯ hours ÷ 24 = ⬡ days ⬡ hours

Total = ⬡ days ⬡ hours + ⬠ days = ☐ days ☐ hours

1st	2nd	3rd	4th

RECORD SHEET FOR EXPEDITION (VARIATION)

Explorer's name: Colour

_____   [ ]

| CAPITAL CITY stopover | [ ] days |

PLANE speed 300km/h   [ ] 00km ÷ speed = [•] hours

OASIS TOWN stopover   [ ] days

LAND ROVER speed 50km/h [ ] 00km ÷ speed = [•] hours

RIVERVILLE stopover   [ ] days

BOAT speed 8km/h   [ ] 0km ÷ speed = [•] hours

HILL HUTS stopover   [ ] days

MULE speed 7km/h   [ ] 0km ÷ speed = [•] hours

CAMP stopover   [ ] days

GUIDED speed 3km/h   [ ] km ÷ speed= [•] hours

My expedition took:

[ ] days (for stopovers) + [•] hours (for journeys)

= [ ] days [ ] hours

| 1st | 2nd | 3rd | 4th |

BOOMERANG

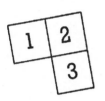

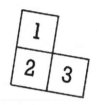

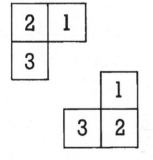

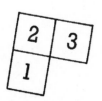

TEACHING CONTENT

★ Recognising rotating shapes and patterns (SSM: 3a; PM: D)
★ Visualising movements of a particular pattern (SSM: 3a; PM: D)
★ Plotting on a number grid (SSM: 3b; PM: B)

PREPARATION

Assembling the game: This is a pencil-and-paper game for two players.
The game sheet (photocopiable page 117) can be cut into two game
strips for two separate games. The players need a game strip, a different-
coloured pen each, two dice and a shaker, the 'How to play' sheet and a
black pen. Light-coloured pens are best as they do not intrude too much
on the grid, and a wrongly coloured square is much easier to sort out if it
is coloured in yellow or pink rather than in blue or purple.

Introducing the game: Talk about boomerangs. How much do the
children know about them, especially their property of returning to the
thrower? The 'boomerangs' in this game are composed of three squares
giving a simple boomerang shape. Discuss how the shape can be in any
form (see illustration opposite).

HOW TO PLAY

Each player in turn throws both the dice and then chooses which square
to colour in on the grid (unless, of course, a double number is thrown). If
2 and 5 are thrown, for example, the 2 can be used on the horizontal line
and the 5 on the vertical or vice versa (2, 5 or 5, 2). The aim of this game
is to get blocks of three squares in your colour together in a boomerang
shape and, conversely, to stop one's opponent's attempts to do the same.
The choice of square allows for some limited tactical play when an
opponent is near to having a complete boomerang. When a boomerang
is spotted (and it is the responsibility of each player to recognise her own
boomerang), its three squares are outlined in black. If both the possible
squares thrown are already coloured, play passes to the other player. The
first player to get three boomerangs wins.

TEACHER'S ROLE

After the game, ask pertinent questions about the rotation of the shapes.
Is there a right or wrong way up? Go on to look at the central square of
the boomerang shape and show how it rotates to give the appearance
that the boomerang has changed its shape. Has it really changed its
shape? Make a similar boomerang on larger squared paper and show
how the two 'wings' seem to move around the centre as the boomerang
is rotated. Make other shapes from squared paper using more squares,
such as zigzag or T-shapes, and any other shapes with definite 'wings'.
Cut them out and then rotate them about a specific square by putting a
drawing pin through it and moving the shape around. If the children are
responsive, the idea of moving through angles or degrees may be
introduced. In this game the shapes have moved through right angles
and this would be an obvious beginning for the children's own shapes. At
each new rotation, outline the shape – rotating through a full circle gives
four shapes around one centre, making a sort of flower shape.

HOW TO PLAY BOOMERANG

For 2 players only

YOU NEED: a game sheet, two dice and a shaker, a different light-coloured pen each and a black pen.

❶ Throw both the dice.

❷ Use the two dice numbers to choose a square. There could be two choices.

So, if 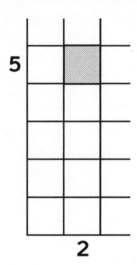 *are thrown, you can colour:*

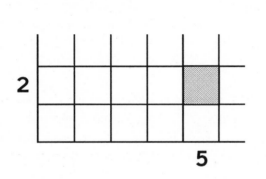

or

❸ Choose one square to colour in. You are aiming to colour in three squares to make a boomerang shape.

❹ If both possible squares are already coloured, play passes to the other player.

❺ When a boomerang shape is made, draw a black line around it.

❻The first player to get three boomerangs wins.

GAME SHEETS FOR BOOMERANG

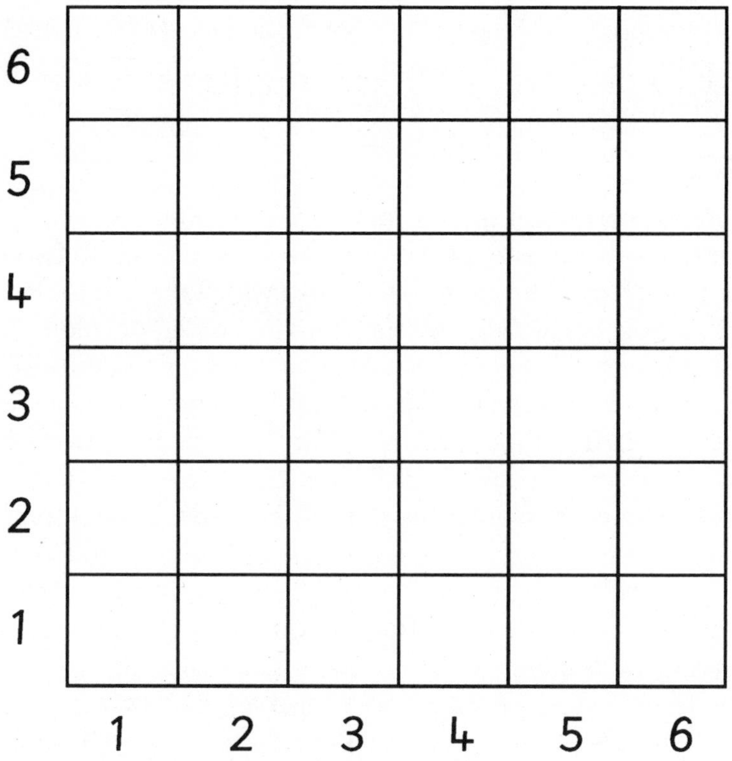

Name _____

Colour

Name _____

Colour

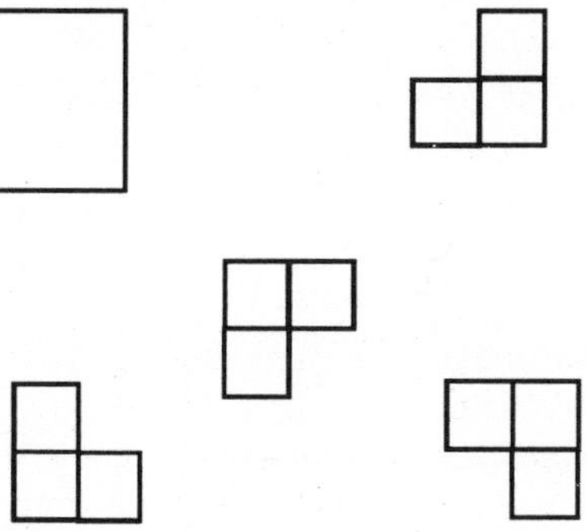

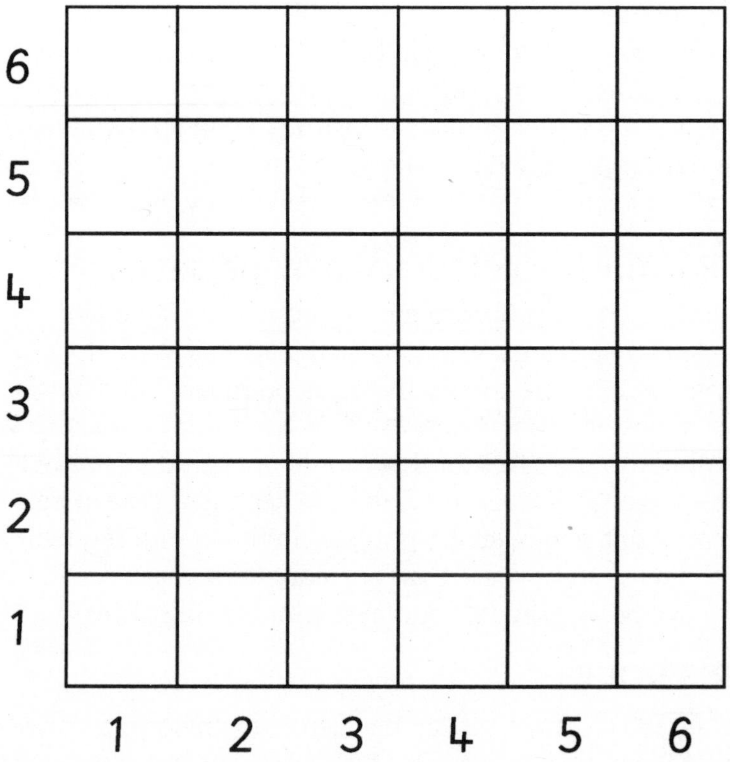

6

5

4

3

2

1

    1   2   3   4   5   6

Name _____

Colour

Name _____

Colour

6

5

4

3

2

1

    1   2   3   4   5   6

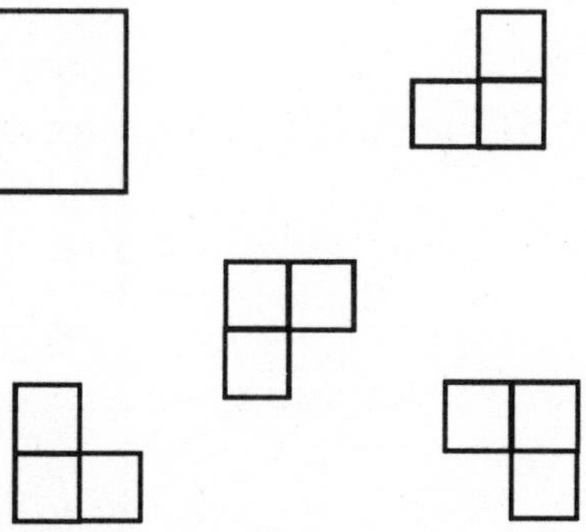

HAPPY BIRTHDAY

TEACHING CONTENT

☆ Seeing the composition of the year as months and weeks (SSM: 4a; T: B)
☆ Expressing birthdays conventionally as days and months (SSM: 4a; T: C)
☆ Using different types of calendar (SSM: 4b; T:C)

PREPARATION

Assembling the game: Mount the two halves of the game board (photocopiable pages 120 and 121) on to an A3 board or on to two A4 sheets of card which can be held together with wide tape and folded like a chessboard. Colour each corner of the board in a different colour, as indicated. Each player will need a coloured counter matching one of these corners. Copy the birthday cakes sheet (photocopiable page 122) directly on to thin card or mount it firmly. Cut the sheet into squares and give one 'cake' to every child in the class. In order to use 'real' data for this game, ask them each to enter the date and number of the month of their birthday on to their cake. The 'icing' edge can be coloured in and the child's name written on the back. Spare cakes can have teachers' or other children's birthdays on them. The distribution of class birthdays may be biased towards a four or six month period, owing to the school's intake policy. There should be about three cakes for each month, so cull birthdays for the spare cakes from the school register to fill in any empty months. Try to get each birthday on a different date. Put the class number on the back of cakes for children from other classes and note adults by the use of Mr, Miss, Mrs or Ms. The record sheet for this game (photocopiable page 123) is optional. If you choose to use it, you will need one sheet for the group and a different-coloured pen (preferably matching the counters/corners) for each child.

Introducing the game: If there is a gap between completing the cakes and playing the game, before playing, ask the children how many months there are in the year and what their names are in sequence. Point out how the track round the board shows the number of weeks in each month with the last space in each month showing any 'left over' days.

HOW TO PLAY

Stack the cakes in their appropriate month segments: all the January cakes on the January picture and so on. Each player picks a coloured counter/corner and, in turn, throws the dice and moves her counter starting from the heavier New Year's Day line. When she stops on a week, she can look through the cakes for that month and see if any have a birthday date in the same week. If so, she can keep that cake in her colour 'corner'. If not, the cakes are put back in the month segment and play goes on. There can be more than one counter on each week. When all the cakes have been claimed, the player with the most wins.

TEACHER'S ROLE

After the game, the record sheet can be filled in by the group drawing in 'cakes' (large dots) in their colours on the appropriate date spaces. This gives them experience of using yet another type of calendar. Explain how this calendar cannot show the weeks consecutively.

PHOTOCOPIABLE PAGES
Happy birthday game board sheets 120 and 121, birthday cakes sheet 122, 'How to play' sheet 119, group record sheet 123 (optional).

FOR CONSTRUCTION
Thick A3 card (or two sheets A4 and some wide sticky tape), thin card, adhesive, scissors, pens or pencils.

FOR PLAYING
Happy birthday game board, a dice and shaker, the completed birthday cakes (see 'Preparation'), a different-coloured counter for each player.

HOW TO PLAY HAPPY BIRTHDAY

For 2 to 4 players

YOU NEED: Happy birthday game board, completed birthday cakes, a dice and shaker, a different-coloured counter for each player.

❶ Stack the cakes on the right months: cakes for January birthdays on January on the board, and so on.

❷ Pick a colour corner and a counter each.

❸ In turn, throw the dice and move your counter round the board that number of weeks, starting at the New Year's Day line.

❹ When you stop on a week, look among that month's cakes for a cake with a birthday in the week you have landed on.

❺ If you find a cake, put it in your colour corner. If not, play goes on to the next player.

❻ There can be more than one counter on a week.

❼ Play until all the cakes are claimed. The player with the most cakes wins.

HAPPY BIRTHDAY GAME BOARD

red

blue

green

yellow

BIRTHDAY CAKES

Enter birthday like this:

Date to the left:
e.g., 21
Month to the right:
e.g., 11

RECORD SHEET FOR HAPPY BIRTHDAY

| red | Name _____ | | green | Name _____ |
| blue | Name _____ | | yellow | Name _____ |

Jan	Feb	Mar	Apr	May	June	July	Aug	Sep	Oct	Nov	Dec
1	1	1	1	1	1	1	1	1	1	1	1
2	2	2	2	2	2	2	2	2	2	2	2
3	3	3	3	3	3	3	3	3	3	3	3
4	4	4	4	4	4	4	4	4	4	4	4
5	5	5	5	5	5	5	5	5	5	5	5
6	6	6	6	6	6	6	6	6	6	6	6
7	7	7	7	7	7	7	7	7	7	7	7
8	8	8	8	8	8	8	8	8	8	8	8
9	9	9	9	9	9	9	9	9	9	9	9
10	10	10	10	10	10	10	10	10	10	10	10
11	11	11	11	11	11	11	11	11	11	11	11
12	12	12	12	12	12	12	12	12	12	12	12
13	13	13	13	13	13	13	13	13	13	13	13
14	14	14	14	14	14	14	14	14	14	14	14
15	15	15	15	15	15	15	15	15	15	15	15
16	16	16	16	16	16	16	16	16	16	16	16
17	17	17	17	17	17	17	17	17	17	17	17
18	18	18	18	18	18	18	18	18	18	18	18
19	19	19	19	19	19	19	19	19	19	19	19
20	20	20	20	20	20	20	20	20	20	20	20
21	21	21	21	21	21	21	21	21	21	21	21
22	22	22	22	22	22	22	22	22	22	22	22
23	23	23	23	23	23	23	23	23	23	23	23
24	24	24	24	24	24	24	24	24	24	24	24
25	25	25	25	25	25	25	25	25	25	25	25
26	26	26	26	26	26	26	26	26	26	26	26
27	27	27	27	27	27	27	27	27	27	27	27
28	28	28	28	28	28	28	28	28	28	28	28
29	29 leap year	29	29	29	29	29	29	29	29	29	29
30		30	30	30	30	30	30	30	30	30	30
31		31		31		31	31		31		31

EURO TOUR

TEACHING CONTENT

☆ Measuring distances on a map using a scale ruler
   (SSM: 4a and 4b; PM: D/E)
☆ Working out comparative 'speeds' of journeys (SSM: 4a; PM: E)
☆ Familiarising children with the capital cities of Europe and their
   locations

WHAT YOU NEED

PHOTOCOPIABLE PAGES
Record strips and scale ruler sheet 127, 'How to play' and aeroplane playing pieces sheet 126.

FOR CONSTRUCTION
Card, scissors, adhesive, coloured pens or crayons to match counters.

FOR PLAYING
Euro tour A3 colour pull-out game board, aeroplane playing pieces, a dice and shaker, six coloured counters and a pencil and a record strip for each player, the scale ruler, a calculator.

PREPARATION

Assembling the game: For this game you will need the A3 colour pull-out game board given at the back of this book. You may wish to mount this on to card and laminate it to protect it further. The scale ruler (photocopiable sheet 127) should be mounted on to a piece of stiff card. Each player will also need a 'Euro tour ticket' (a record strip on which to enter his five journeys) and an aeroplane playing piece (photocopiable page 126). Cut out the aeroplanes and colour them each in a different colour. Then assemble them as shown below:

Stick and hold with a paper clip until the adhesive drys.

Introducing the game: While the children should know about and have had experience of simple plans and scales, such as a plan of the classroom, 'Euro tour' may be an introduction to using an atlas-type map. Talk about going on holiday and travelling by air. Bring in postcards. One of the fun elements of the game is 'sending a postcard' from every city visited.

HOW TO PLAY

Each player has an aeroplane playing piece and six coloured counters for 'postcards'. It would be useful if each player's set of counters and aeroplane were the same colour and different from each other's. A 5 or 6 has to be thrown to start. The players can start from any city they like unless there is an aeroplane already on it. Each player immediately puts one of his counters on the postcard from his start city. At no time in the game can two aeroplanes be on the same city – we don't want any mid-air crashes on the trips! To move from one city to another, a player throws the dice and moves along the route with the same number. When he gets to a city, he puts one of his counters on the matching postcard. It doesn't matter if someone else's counter is there already. If the number thrown does not have a route, or if there is a plane on the destination, the player stays where he is. The players cannot go back to cities they have already visited. As they travel round, the players must fill in the names of their flights on their recording strips, but leave the distances blank. When a player has visited five cities, he must stop travelling and wait until everyone else has finished. Finally, the players measure the distances travelled using the scale ruler and complete their record strips. The player who has travelled the furthest wins.

TEACHER'S ROLE

The mechanics of the game are fairly straightforward, but a certain degree of strategy is called for. It might be instructive to observe which children latch on to London as the ideal starting point as it alone has six routes. When the children are measuring get them to co-operate. There is only one scale ruler and even if every child has one each, there isn't room on the board for everyone to measure together. Encourage them to take it in turns to measure the distances and to use their measurements for the whole group.

GAME VARIATIONS

• If the players are allowed to go to destinations they have already visited, greater distances may be covered before the five city rule stops play. Instead of a record strip use a plain paper record with each journey listed on it. Use the record strip as a model.

• 'Speed' can be introduced by setting an average flight speed and a stopover time at each city; for example, a flight speed of 650 km/h (allowing for landings and take-offs) and a stopover time of 10 hours (allowing for a whirlwind tour of the city and the buying of a postcard). In this case you may want to standardise the distances and there is a table of distances which corresponds to those of the map given below. These are not the true air distances necessarily (which take curved paths and so on), but are simple 'on the map' distances and are very approximate.

Table of distances	
London–Dublin	480km
London–Reykjavik	1860km
London–Oslo	1200km
London–Amsterdam	360km
London–Paris	360km
London–Madrid	1320km
Paris–Madrid	1080km
Paris–Geneva	420km
Paris–Vienna	1080km
Geneva–Rome	720km
Rome–Berlin	1200km
Rome–Athens	1020km
Rome–Amsterdam	1320km
Athens–Vienna	1260km
Athens–Warsaw	1680km
Warsaw–Berlin	600km
Warsaw–Copenhagen	660km
Berlin–Amsterdam	600km
Amsterdam–Copenhagen	600km
Copenhagen–Oslo	600km
Copenhagen–Stockholm	600km
Stockholm–Oslo	420km
Oslo–Reykjavik	1740km
Madrid–Rome	1500km
Madrid–Lisbon	480km

GAMES

HOW TO PLAY EURO TOUR

For 2 or more players

YOU NEED: A3 colour game board, six same-coloured counters and an aeroplane playing piece each, scale ruler, calculator and a 'Euro tour ticket' each.

❶ Throw a ⚃ or ⚅ to start.

❷ Pick any city to start unless it has an aeroplane on it already. Put a counter on the postcard of your starting city.

❸ To move, throw the dice and go along the route with the same number. Put a counter on the postcard of the city you reach.

❹ Fill in your journeys on your 'Euro tour ticket', but LEAVE THE DISTANCES BLANK.

❺ If a number thrown does not have a route, wait for another go.

❻ If there is an aeroplane at the destination of your route, wait for another go.

❼ You CANNOT GO BACK TO A CITY YOU HAVE ALREADY VISITED.

❽ When everyone has been to five cities, measure the distances travelled and complete your tickets.

❾ The player who travelled the furthest wins.

PLAYING PIECES

green			green	blue			blue
yellow			yellow	red			red

PHOTOCOPIABLE GAMES

EURO TOUR

RECORD SHEET FOR EURO TOUR

Euro tour ticket			Passenger's name
From	To	km	

Total km [ ]

| 1st | 2nd | 3rd | 4th |

Euro tour ticket			Passenger's name
From	To	km	

Total km [ ]

| 1st | 2nd | 3rd | 4th |

Euro tour ticket			Passenger's name
From	To	km	

Total km [ ]

| 1st | 2nd | 3rd | 4th |

Euro tour ticket			Passenger's name
From	To	km	

Total km [ ]

| 1st | 2nd | 3rd | 4th |

0   120   240   360   480   600   720   840   960   1080   1200   1320   1440   1560   1680   1800   1920   2040   km

Scale: 1 centimetre = 120 kilometres

127

THE FAIRY RING

TEACHING CONTENT

☆ Using degrees of turn (SSM: 3c; PM: B)
☆ Using the eight point compass (PM: D)

WHAT YOU NEED

PHOTOCOPIABLE PAGES
'How to play' sheet 130, record sheet 132, direction cards and playing pieces sheet 131.

FOR CONSTRUCTION
Thick and thin card, scissors, adhesive, paper clips (or staples).

FOR PLAYING
The Fairy Ring A3 colour pull-out game board, a dice and shaker, one counter, a direction card (for degrees or compass points), a playing piece (or counter) and record sheet for each player.

PREPARATION

Assembling the game: Mount the A3 colour pull-out game board from the back of this book on to card and laminate it if you wish. Assemble the playing pieces and cut out the direction card(s). These are best copied directly on to card. Cut out the playing pieces and fold them up. Staple the two halves together near the base (this also adds weight) or stick the pieces together, holding them with paper clips until they are dry. The record sheet and 'How to play' sheet can be amended to show different objectives if necessary (see 'Game variations'). The players could use different-coloured counters instead of the playing pieces, if you prefer.
Introducing the game: Before playing this game, make sure that the players understand about the angle of turn (be it degrees or compass points) always being made from the top vertical line of the 'stars' on the board. Show the children how to use the direction card and make sure that they understand the method of moving the playing pieces/counters around the board.

HOW TO PLAY

Each player needs a playing piece and a record sheet. The players all start in the Fairy Ring. In turn, each player throws the dice and moves the counter that number round the direction card. The players must move their playing pieces from the Fairy Ring to the first place on the board in the direction shown. They will stay there until the next round of dice throws. To move again, the players must first throw a number bigger than that shown at their current location. If they do not, they must throw the dice again and again until they do. For every useless throw they must cross out one item of food or a level of drink on their record sheets. If they run out of food and drink before returning to the Fairy Ring the players are stuck at their last locations 'for ever'. When they have thrown the bigger number, they can throw the dice to use the direction card to find out the next direction. If there is no place in the direction shown or if the place is already occupied, the players must stay where they are until it is their turn again. If they land on the Fairy Ring, they can go in any direction they like. At each place they visit the players should cross it off their record sheets. The first player to visit and leave five places and return to the Fairy Ring wins. Continue until everyone is either back to the Fairy Ring and off the Desolate Moor or doomed to wander there 'for ever'.

TEACHER'S ROLE

This is a game which, if played correctly, becomes self-teaching. During the game, ask the players which places they are aiming for and which are desirable. (Places with low dice numbers should be the answer, as they are easier to get off.) After the game, pose questions such as, 'If a traveller was at the Monolith, which direction would he or she need to get to visit the Hermit's Hut?' Ask the children which places are in which sectors of the map; for example, for degrees, places between 0° and 90°, or, for the compass points, places between north and east. Combine sectors. Which places lie on straight lines to each other, for example, the Enchanter's Tower, the Bottomless Marsh, the Monolith and the Broken Cross? Which line or lines go through the Fairy Ring?

GAME VARIATIONS

• The game can be played in a short, almost express, form where the record sheet is not used. Instead of visiting five different places, each player has to leave and then get back to the Fairy Ring, but still with the same rule of having to throw a higher number to leave a specific place. The first player to get back to the Fairy Ring wins.

• The record sheet version can be lengthened by requiring the players to visit four different places and cross them off on their sheets in a line: vertically, horizontally or diagonally.

• The game can be played as a solo version of the shortened game with the child using the record sheet and trying to leave and get back to the Fairy Ring before her supplies run out.

HOW TO PLAY THE FAIRY RING

For 2 to 4 players

YOU NEED: the A3 colour game board, a direction card, one counter, a playing piece and a record sheet for each player, a dice and shaker.

You have stepped into a Fairy Ring and it has carried you away on to the Desolate Moor.

❶ Start from the Fairy Ring.

❷ Throw the dice. Move the counter that number round on the direction card.

❸ Go in the direction it shows and stop at the first available place.

❹ If there is no place in the direction shown, or if the place is already occupied, stay where you are until the next round.

❺ To move on in the next round, you must first throw a bigger number than is shown at your current place. Keep throwing the dice until you do, but for every useless throw cross out one item of food or a level of drink from your record sheet. If you use up all your food and drink before returning to the Fairy Ring, you are doomed to stay on the Desolate Moor for ever!

❻ When you have thrown the bigger number, cross the place you are leaving off your record sheet. Then throw the dice again to use the direction card and find out your next direction.

❼ If you land on the Fairy Ring, you can go in any direction.

❽ The first player to visit and leave five places and return to the Fairy Ring is the winner.

❾ Continue playing until everyone is either off the Desolate Moor or doomed to wander there for ever!

DIRECTION CARDS AND PLAYING PIECES

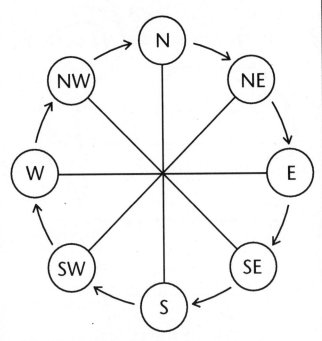

DIRECTION CARD
Compass points

To use this direction card:
1 Put counter on N.
2 Throw the dice and move the counter round clockwise for that number.
3 The next player goes on round the card from this circle.
4 Go in the direction shown.

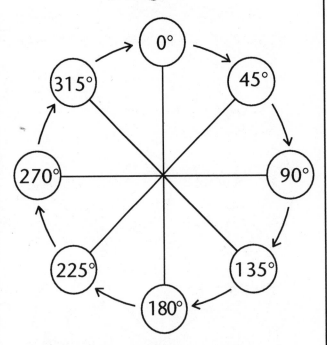

DIRECTION CARD
Degrees

To use this direction card:
1 Put counter on 0°.
2 Throw the dice and move the counter round clockwise for that number.
3 The next player goes on round the card from this circle.
4 Go in the direction shown.

Stick and hold with a paper clip until the adhesive is dry.

yellow			green yellow
green			green
blue			blue
red			red

RECORD SHEET FOR THE FAIRY RING

FOOD

DRINK

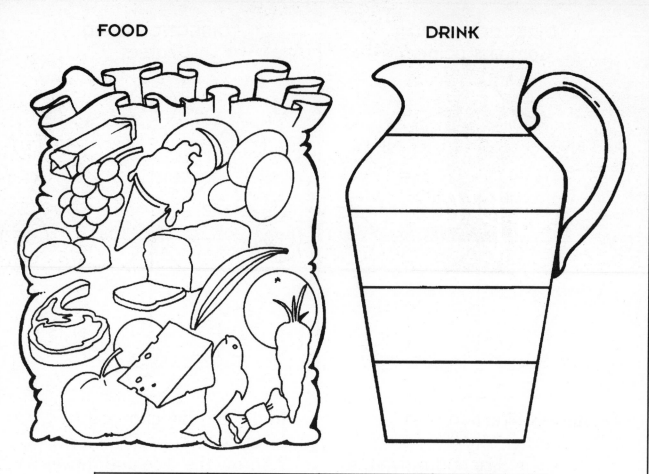

Stricken Oak	Broken Cross	Dwarf's Mine	Ruined Church
Cave of Eyes	Monolith	Tottering Stone	Two Larches
Bottomless Marsh	Stepping Stones	Abandoned Sheepfold	Ancient Barrow
Enchanter's Tower	Cairn	Hermit's Hut	Crumbling Cliff

Special section

ABOUT THIS SECTION

Besides providing apparatus integral to some of the games in this book, the material in this Special Section is designed to help the development of map-reading and its attendant mathematical skill of measuring angles and bearings. Starting from the simple identification of 'real-life' right angles using Croc Chops (photocopiable page 141) to measuring bearings and distances on 'home-made' maps, the children are encouraged to look at maps afresh. The grid layout (photocopiable page 138) brings home the importance of transcribing the location of places in universally understood methods, starting at a simple letter and number level and leading to sophisticated four- and six-figure references, a skill which closely parallels plotting positions on the horizontal and vertical axes of graphs. The stand-up OS map symbols (photocopiable pages 139 and 140) make the link between real features and their abstract representation on a map. Indeed, these symbols, allied with the grid (photocopiable page 138), can be used to build simulated landscapes which can be investigated by the children as a classroom-based activity, before transferring their skills to the countryside.

Besides fostering the links between mathematics and geography, the apparatus in this section can be adapted easily for surveying simply the positions and features of the school landscape. Furthermore, these skills can be extended to be part of outdoor and adventurous activities using maps and compass-reading.

THE GRID

The blank grid on photocopiable page 138 has a six letter baseline with ten numbered rows. The grid is best mounted or copied directly on to card and then laminated. The random selection of a square on the grid is a special two-way process of finding a letter by using a letter dice and choosing a number by drawing out a number square from a bag. To make a letter dice, use an ordinary six-sided dice with sticky labels covering the dots. Relabel the faces A to F. For the number squares you could use the 0 to 9 digital cards of the 'Degree randomiser' (photocopiable page 142) with the 0 made into 10. Develop this further by amending the grid so that it has only letters or numbers. The children must always identify a square by giving the base letter first. The same is true for number grids, thereby employing the 'eastings' shorthand used by the Ordnance Survey.

However, these systems identify a square rather than a single point. To find a point within a square, it is necessary to use the lines of the grid. This is not as difficult a transition as might be supposed. To take the children towards OS grid references, draw their attention to the nine lines sub-dividing each large square in effect making each square into a miniature grid. Delete the letters and numbers given and insert letters on the grid lines as shown in the illustration opposite.

Encourage the children to play a game using the letter dice and number cards as before, except that 0 is used as 0 not 10, coloured pens, pencils and a copy of this modified grid each. In turn, the players secretly throw a letter (the baseline letter) and pick a number

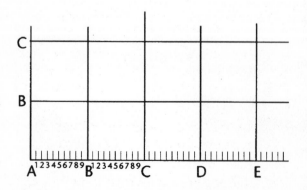

Relabelling with letters on the grid lines.

(the small divisions on the baseline) and then repeat the process for the vertical position. The child locates these lines and identifies the point on the grid with a coloured dot and writes down its location for reference, for example A8B7. Then he reads out the reference which his opponent must try to pencil in on her grid. The two grids can be compared to see if the point is in the right place. In time, the players will dispense with the dice and number cards and make up the references for themselves. Alternatively, for a whole class game you could make up lists of references for the children to plot on shared grids. Once finished, the children's grids can be compared with the teacher's master copy.

Once the children show competence with letters and numbers, wean them on to all number grids. This done, the children will have been introduced to four-figure grid references.

Move on to look at real maps of real places. Make a number of four- or six-digit grid reference cards to use with maps of your locality and ask the children to find what is located at each reference. Most schools should have local OS maps at 1:50 000 (Landranger) and 1:25 000 (Pathfinder) scales and, ideally, 1:10 000 (Nationwide Large Scale) and 1:2 500 (Rural Area Large Scale) or 1:1 250 (Urban Area Large Scale).

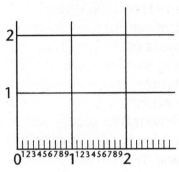

Relabelling the grid with numbers.

3-D OS MAP SYMBOL CARDS

While Ordnance Survey (OS) map symbols may seem quite complicated for primary-age children, the reality is that maps are covered in symbols. The stand-up 3-D OS map symbol cards (photocopiable pages 139 and 140) are meant to improve understanding of a particular symbol by associating it with its three-dimensional counterpart in a child-friendly manner. When the cards are viewed from above, the symbols can be seen in full and can be linked to those on maps. Besides the game described in the text ('Anywhere', pages 83–85), the cards can be used to make model villages and towns on a sheet of plain paper or card which in themselves form instant maps which only need additional roads, railways, rivers and canals drawn on and features shown on the cards, such as cliffs, pylons and footpaths, to be extended. Another activity might be to identify those symbols which are symmetrical and those which are not. The upright section of each card makes this simpler than it might be.

Buildings including houses			Town Hall	Ruin	School	Hospital
Cemetery	Cliff	Milestone	Church with tower	Church with spire	Chapel	Windmill
Golf course	Camp site	Caravan site	Castle	Footpath	Telephone	Railway bridge over road

Canal aqueduct over railway	Public house (pub)	Glasshouse (green house)	Coniferous wood	Picnic site	Bus or railway station	Electricity line with pylons
Radio or TV mast	Chimney or tower	Post office	Heliport	Windpump	Quarry	Level crossing
Railway tunnel	Lighthouse	Deciduous wood	Railway viaduct over river	Railway bridge over river		

Key to layout of OS map symbols

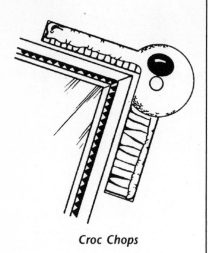

Croc Chops

Degree randomiser and digital cards

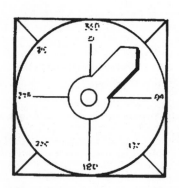

Map compass showing angles

Croc Chops

The easiest angle to become familiar with is the right angle. Croc Chops (photocopiable page 141) is a fun item which allows children to measure the right angles in real objects. When the Croc Chops' jaws are open at right angles, the eye is fully open. Croc Chops is best mounted on to fairly stiff card. Cutting out the open eye will be difficult for some children and they may need assistance. One way round this is to let the children paste the Croc Chops on to card and colour them in class and, when they are dry, send the children home with them for the Croc Chops' eyes to be cut out there. If you do this, keep a few spares in school to replace the ones that don't come back! Another answer is to get the assistance of some older children at lunch-time and cut them out then. Assemble the two halves of each Croc Chops with a paper fastener. Attach a piece of sticky tape to the back of the head to cover and hold in place the back of the paper fastener. This will also help to protect the children's fingers. Every child should have his own Croc Chops.

Degree randomiser

Once the children move on to games where measuring angles uses degrees, there will be a problem getting random numbers fitting 360° or 90°. The degree randomiser (photocopiable page 142) does this by means of digital cards which can be drawn from a bag and put on to a card in a sequence of ones, tens and hundreds, which also help the players to understand the number as it 'grows'. A 90° randomiser can be made by deleting the third digital card space and its associated printing from the randomiser. The digital cards can be kept the same, but if you want to 'even out the chances' do not include the 0 to 3 cards at the beginning of the set. A simple additional activity for the children is to pick random angles using the degree randomiser and draw them using the 90° quadrant and the bearings compass in this section (photocopiable page 144).

Map compasses and dice nets

Direction on a map can be determined by using either bearings (degrees read from north or 0) or by compass points. The two compasses given on photocopiable page 143 show the main bearings at 45° intervals and the eight points of the compass respectively. These compasses can be used with the dice provided or to support the games in this book that explore position and movement, such as 'The Fairy Ring' (pages 128–132). Copy the page on to card. Cut out the compasses and pointers. Attach a pointer to each compass with a paper fastener, held in place with tape across the back. To make the dice, copy the nets on to card and cut them out. Hold the tabs in place with paper clips until the adhesive is dry.

These compasses and dice can be used in game situations or for exploring any map. Having chosen which compass and dice to use, ask a child to throw the dice and choose one of the directions shown. The dice have two angles/compass points on each face to give a choice of direction. The bearings dice has 0° on two faces to emphasise the 0 position. In reality a 0° bearing would not exist as 360° would be used, but it is included here to give a starting point. You may prefer to replace it with 'Miss a turn' as on the compass points dice. Align the compass with north on the map (or the top for the children's creations) and then move the pointer to show the chosen direction: What will you pass if you travel that way? Would another direction be less steep? Put a ruler across the compass and map to help the children to sight along that route.

90° Quadrant

90° quadrant

The 90° quadrant (given on photocopiable page 144) is a right angle, where the individual degrees are plain to see and use. Besides the game 'UFO' in the Photocopiable Games section (pages 89–91), the 90° quadrant and pointer can be mounted on to medium-thick card and assembled with a paper fastener. Put sticky tape across the back of the fastener to hold it in place and protect the children's fingers. It can then be used by the children to work out horizontal and vertical directions. It would be ideal for every child to have one. The pointer is for sighting as on a gun. The cut-off section can be folded up for this purpose.

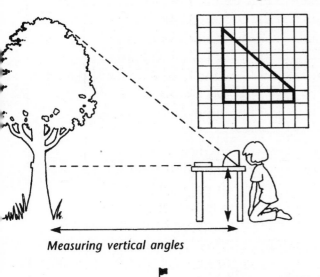

Measuring vertical angles

The 90° quadrant can be used as a 'theodolite' for measuring horizontal angles or as a 'clinometer' for measuring vertical angles. In the latter case it will need to be set level using a spirit level before use. The heights of objects can be ascertained by measuring the angle to the top of the object, say a tree, and measuring the distance to it from the quadrant. Also measure the height of the quadrant from the ground. Draw the whole thing to scale on a large sheet of squared paper including the height of the quadrant. Measure the scale height of the object from the drawing and calculate its true height.

Horizontal mapping of the relative positions of two objects can be done by sighting along the base line to one object and then swinging the pointer round to line up with the second object. This gives the angle between them. Measure the distances from the quadrant to the first object and then from the quadrant to the second object and as a check from first to second object. Draw the angle on a large sheet of paper and measure scale distances to the two objects. If all the operations are done correctly the line from first object to second should be approximately the same as the real measurement. This demonstrates an important element of all land survey that is some kind of self-checking device.

Measuring horizontal angles

Bearings compass

Bearings seem very formidable to many people. Even though modern compasses have very simple explanations on their use, even experienced users can be confused by them. The bearings compass (given on photocopiable page 144) approaches the problem with two objectives: one to familiarise children with the 360° circle and second to show them that from it not only direction, but also distance, can be determined as it incorporates a scale ruler (something a real compass does not). Copy the compass and pointer on to card and mount the pointer in the centre of the compass with a paper fastener. Stick a piece of tape across the back of the fastener on to the back of the compass to hold it in place and to protect the children's fingers.

Draw lines along folds. Line up compass in the centre and fasten pointer through the compass and map.

Use this compass on real maps or let the children draw their own map on a large sheet of paper folded in four and mount the compass and pointer in the middle, as shown opposite. Using the degree randomiser given on page 142 they can make up angles and draw out digital cards to choose distances. They can then use the bearings compass to find the point so identified on their map – what is there?

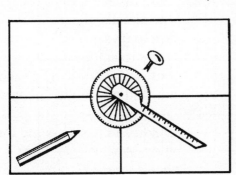

PHOTOCOPIABLE GRID

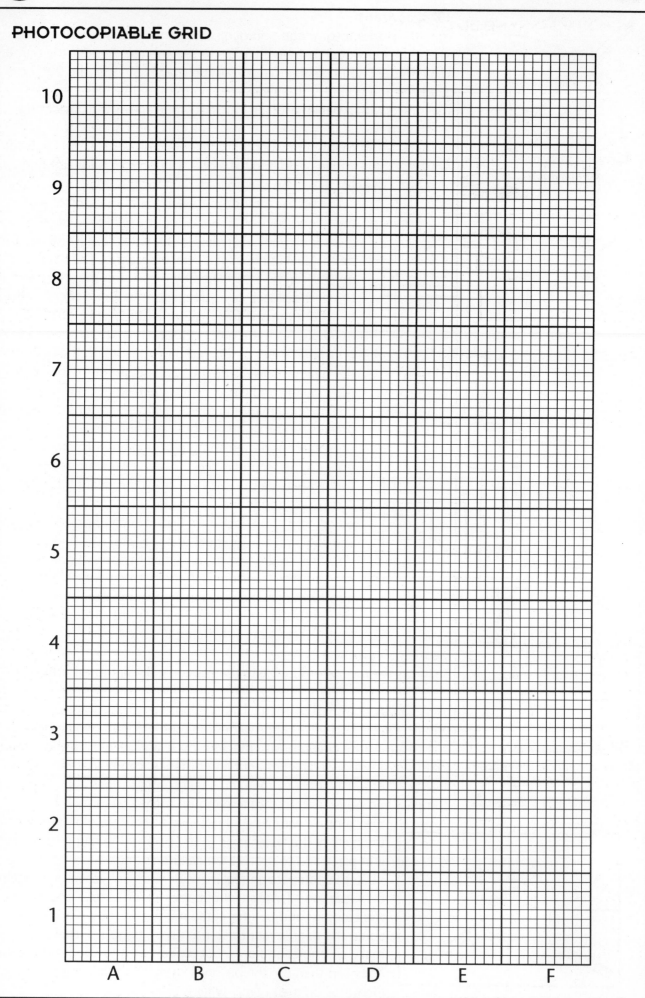

3-D OS MAP SYMBOL CARDS

Map symbols © Ordnance Survey

3-D OS MAP SYMBOL CARDS

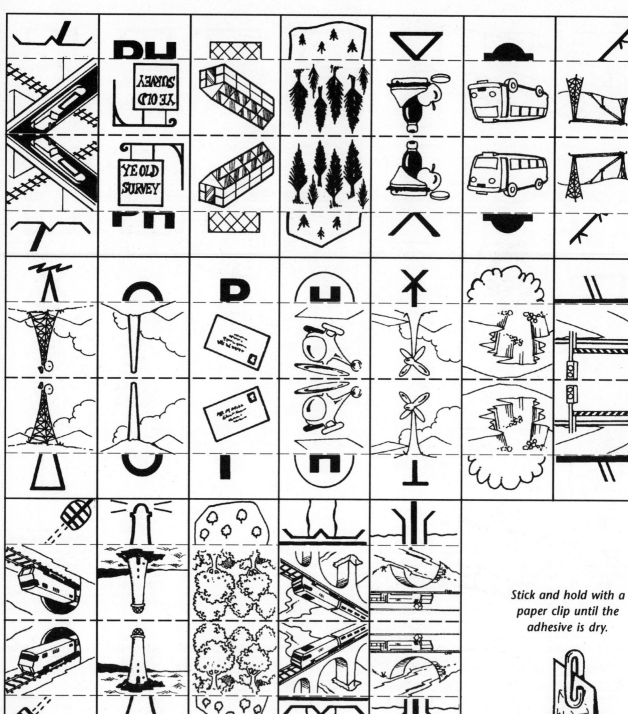

Map symbols © Ordnance Survey

Stick and hold with a paper clip until the adhesive is dry.

Make sure that the two halves of each symbol align when seen from above.

CROC CHOPS PHOTOCOPIABLE

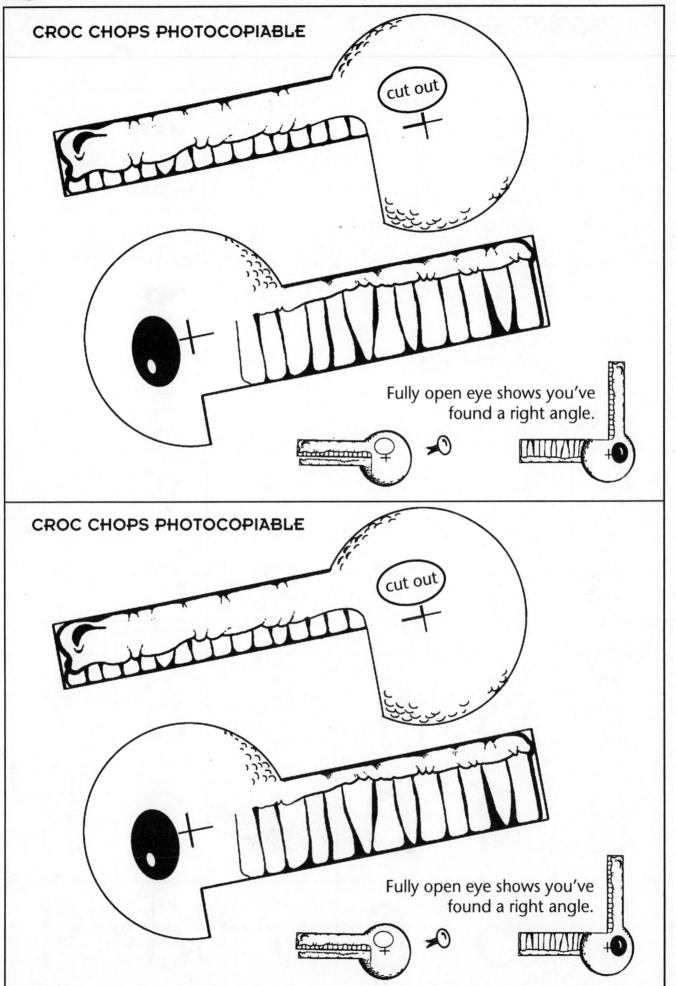

Fully open eye shows you've found a right angle.

CROC CHOPS PHOTOCOPIABLE

Fully open eye shows you've found a right angle.

DEGREE RANDOMISER

3rd card	**2nd card**	**1st card**

3rd card
(if applicable)
If you draw 4,
5, 6, 7, 8 or 9
go again until
0 or 1 or 2 or
3 are drawn.

DIGITAL CARDS
Best copied directly on to card. Keep in an opaque bag.

0	1	2	3	0	1
2	3	4	5	6	7
8	9	0	1	2	3
4	5	6	7	8	9

MAP COMPASSES AND DICE NETS

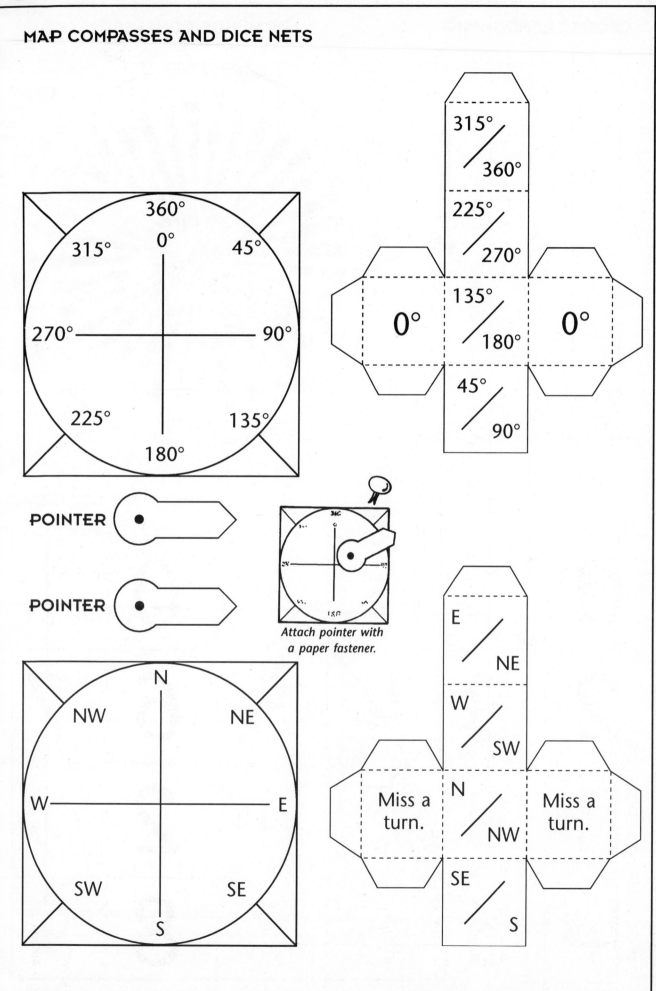

POINTER

POINTER

Attach pointer with
a paper fastener.

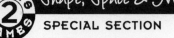

BEARINGS COMPASS

CUT

FOLD OR CUT

BEARINGS COMPASS POINTER

40mm 50 60 70 80 90 100 110 120 130 140 150 160

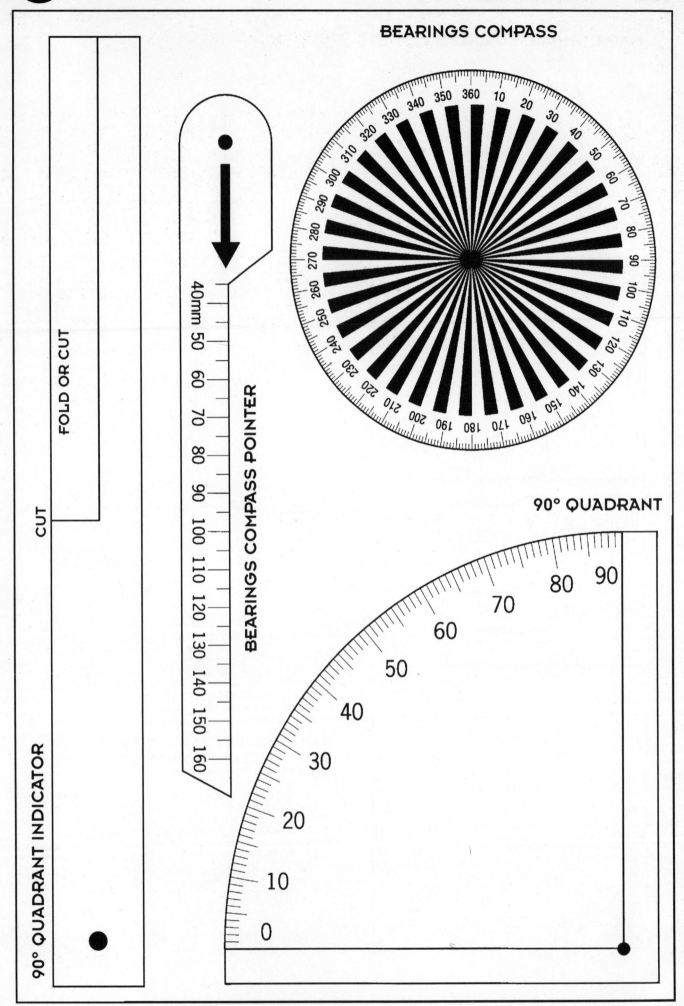

90° QUADRANT

90 80 70 60 50 40 30 20 10 0

90° QUADRANT INDICATOR